Filling Out Forms

by
Mary Ellen Snodgrass

AGS®

American Guidance Service, Inc.
4201 Woodland Road
Circle Pines, MN 55014-1796
1-800-328-2560

Practical English Skills

Printed in the United States of America

ISBN 0–7854–0965–3 (Previously ISBN 0–88671–513–X)

Product Number 90880

A 0 9 8 7 6 5 4 5 3 2

Contents

Introduction

Throughout your lifetime, you will have many new experiences, challenges, and freedoms. With these opportunities come responsibilities.

As you move through life, there are certain skills you will use over and over again. One of these skills is knowing how to fill out a form. You will need to fill out forms to participate in some of life's important activities. You will need to fill out a form to apply for a job, get a driver's license, rent an apartment, or pay your taxes.

In this workbook, you will have an opportunity to see the many different kinds of forms a person must fill out as an independent, productive citizen. As you work through these forms, you will begin to notice that many of them ask for the same basic kinds of information, such as your name, address, phone number, and Social Security number. One thing to remember is that most forms can be filled out successfully if a person reads and follows the instructions carefully. Another important point to remember is to print clearly. A form is sometimes the first contact someone has with you. A neat, correctly completed form that is easy to read creates a positive first impression. Also, forms that are complete and easy to read can help prevent errors as others process your application or work with your form.

This workbook will show you what some kinds of forms look like. The text will also explain why the forms are used or what their value is and will guide you in filing them out. When you have finished this workbook, you will have a better understanding of how to deal with the forms you will face throughout your life.

In addition to filling out forms, this workbook will give you information about and practice in how to shop wisely and how to order from a catalog, how to plan a trip and read transportation schedules, how to choose an apartment, and how to set goals for the future.

First Things First: Learning the Rules

The information in the box below represents many of the questions you'll be asked throughout this book. It can also be used as a "pocket résumé" that will come in handy when filling out many kinds of applications, especially employment applications.

 Information Form: Fill it out now, carefully and completely. Then make a copy to take with you. Keep it in your purse or folded in your wallet. You will be glad you did.

Name _____

Address _____

Telephone Number _____

Social Security Number _____

Driver's License _____

EDUCATION

School _____ Address _____

Degree/Subject _____ Dates _____

School _____ Address _____

Degree/Subject _____ Dates _____

School Activities _____

PREVIOUS EMPLOYMENT (*Summer and part-time jobs*)

Name of Employer _____

Address _____

Job Title _____

Dates _____

Military Service or Draft Status _____

Hobbies and Special Interests _____

Special Skills _____

REFERENCES (*Will need several*) (*Get permission before using names*)

Name _____ Title_____

Address _____

Telephone Number _____

Name _____ Title_____

Address _____

Telephone Number _____

Before you can start to work, you must get a Social Security number. You need this number because your employer must hold back part of your wages so that they can be applied toward your retirement fund. To get a number, you must apply for a card. You can obtain an application, by calling the Social Security office in your area. When you fill out the application, be sure to read it carefully and follow the instructions. Then you will go to the office with your birth certificate and other proof of identification. There is an office in almost every city. Many parents apply for a Social Security card when their baby is born, so you may already have one.

B *Social Security Card Application:* Fill out the following application.

SOCIAL SECURITY ADMINISTRATION
Application for a Social Security Card

Form Approved
OMB No. 0960-0066

INSTRUCTIONS
- Please read "How To Complete This Form" on page 2.
- Print or type using black or blue ink. DO NOT USE PENCIL.
- After you complete this form, take or mail it along with the required documents to your nearest Social Security office.
- If you are completing this form for someone else, answer the questions as they apply to that person. Then, sign your name in question 16.

1 NAME
To Be Shown On Card
FIRST   FULL MIDDLE NAME   LAST

FULL NAME AT BIRTH
IF OTHER THAN ABOVE
FIRST   FULL MIDDLE NAME   LAST

OTHER NAMES USED

2 MAILING ADDRESS
Do Not Abbreviate
STREET ADDRESS, APT. NO., PO BOX, RURAL ROUTE NO.

CITY   STATE   ZIP CODE

3 CITIZENSHIP
(Check One)
☐ U.S. Citizen ☐ Legal Alien Allowed To Work ☐ Legal Alien Not Allowed To Work ☐ Foreign Student Allowed Restricted Employment ☐ Conditionally Legalized Alien Allowed To Work ☐ Other (See Instructions On Page 2)

4 SEX
☐ Male ☐ Female

5 RACE/ETHNIC DESCRIPTION
(Check One Only—Voluntary)
☐ Asian, Asian-American Or Pacific Islander ☐ Hispanic ☐ Black (Not Hispanic) ☐ North American Indian Or Alaskan Native ☐ White (Not Hispanic)

6 DATE OF BIRTH
MONTH DAY YEAR

7 PLACE OF BIRTH
(Do Not Abbreviate)
CITY   STATE OR FOREIGN COUNTRY

FCI   Office Use Only

8 MOTHER'S MAIDEN NAME
FIRST   FULL MIDDLE NAME   LAST NAME AT HER BIRTH

9 FATHER'S NAME
FIRST   FULL MIDDLE NAME   LAST

10 Has the person in item 1 ever received a Social Security number before?
☐ Yes (If "yes", answer questions 11-13.) ☐ No (If "no", go on to question 14.) ☐ Don't Know (If "don't know", go on to question 14.)

11 Enter the Social Security number previously assigned to the person listed in item 1.
☐☐☐ – ☐☐ – ☐☐☐☐

12 Enter the name shown on the most recent Social Security card issued for the person listed in item 1.
FIRST   MIDDLE   LAST

13 Enter any different date of birth if used on an earlier application for a card.
MONTH   DAY   YEAR

14 TODAY'S DATE ▶ MONTH DAY YEAR   **15 DAYTIME PHONE NUMBER** ▶ ( ) AREA CODE

DELIBERATELY FURNISHING (OR CAUSING TO BE FURNISHED) FALSE INFORMATION ON THIS APPLICATION IS A CRIME PUNISHABLE BY FINE OR IMPRISONMENT, OR BOTH.

16 YOUR SIGNATURE
▶

17 YOUR RELATIONSHIP TO THE PERSON IN ITEM 1 IS:
☐ Self ☐ Natural Or Adoptive Parent ☐ Legal Guardian ☐ Other (Specify)

DO NOT WRITE BELOW THIS LINE (FOR SSA USE ONLY)				
NPN	DOC	NTI	CAN	ITV
PBC	EVI	EVA	EVC	PRA	NWR	DNR	UNIT

EVIDENCE SUBMITTED

SIGNATURE AND TITLE OF EMPLOYEE(S) REVIEWING EVIDENCE AND/OR CONDUCTING INTERVIEW

DATE

DCL   DATE

Form SS-5 (9/89) 5/88 edition may be used until supply is exhausted

Let's start with the job application. You should think of it as the first impression an employer will have of you. If your application is sloppy, incorrect, or incomplete, he or she will think the same of you *without even meeting you!* Since most employers receive hundreds of applications a year, common sense tells you that the employer will probably look first at applications that are easy to read and complete and show good handwriting. Your handwriting is especially important if the job requires others to read it. A waiter or waitress, clerk, salesperson, and secretary are some examples. Even employers who do not require much writing want an employee who is neat and thorough. Do not rush through an application!

The following are examples of employment applications. Since the job market is very competitive, your education, special training, and other jobs or experiences will be of interest. So, be thorough, but don't "exaggerate" or give incorrect information. Most employers do check what you tell them, and even a small fib could cost you a job. Remember that on most applications you are asked to print. Also notice that it is common to ask that the last name be written first followed by the first name and middle initial.

FOR OFFICE USE ONLY			FOR OFFICE USE ONLY	
Possible Work Locations	Possible Positions	**EMPLOYMENT QUESTIONNAIRE**	Work Location _____ Position _____	Rate _____ Date

(PLEASE PRINT NEATLY)

Position(s) applied for _____ Rate of pay expected $ _____ per week

Would you work Full Time _____ Part Time_____ Specify days and hours if part time _____

Were you previously employed by us? _____ If yes, when? _____

If your application is considered favorably, on what date will you be available for work? _____19 ___

PERSONAL Date _____

Name _____ Social Security No. _____
      Last   First Initial   Middle Initial

Present address _____ Telephone No. _____
              No.   Street

_____
      City   State   Zip

Notice that the part of the application below asks some personal questions. Some questions such as age, race, or marital status cannot be asked unless there is a special job-related reason to do so.

A *Special Sections of Job Applications:* Fill out the following forms. Read the directions carefully.

To Applicant: READ THIS INTRODUCTION CAREFULLY BEFORE ANSWERING ANY QUESTIONS IN THIS BLOCKED-OFF AREA. The Civil Rights Act of 1964 prohibits discrimination in employment practice because of race, color, religion, sex, or national origin. P.L. 90–202 prohibits discrimination on the basis of age with respect to individuals who are at least 40 but less than 65 years of age. The laws of some states also prohibit some or all of the above type of discrimination.

DO NOT ANSWER ANY QUESTIONS CONTAINED IN THIS BLOCKED-OFF AREA UNLESS THE EMPLOYER HAS CHECKED THE BOX NEXT TO THE QUESTION, thereby indicating that the requested information is needed for a bona fide occupational qualification, national security laws, or other legally permissible reasons.

☐ Are you over the age of twenty–one? _____ If no, hire is subject to verification that you are of a minimum legal age.

☐ Sex: M _____ F _____   ☐ Height _____ ft. _____ in.   ☐ Weight _____ lbs.

☐ Marital Status: Single _____ Engaged _____ Married _____ Separated _____ Divorced _____ Widowed _____

☐ Date of Marriage _____   ☐ Number of dependents including yourself _____

☐ Are you a citizen of the U.S.A.? _____   ☐ What is your present Selective Service classification? _____

☐ Have you ever been bonded? _____ If yes, on what jobs? _____

☐ Have you been convicted of a crime in the past 10 years, excluding misdemeanors and summary offenses? _____

If yes, describe in full _____

Employer may list other bona fide occupational questions on lines below:

☐ _____

☐ _____

Do you have any physical defects which preclude you from performing certain kinds of work? _____ If yes, describe

such defects and specific work limitations. _____

_____

Have you had a major illness in the past 5 years? _____ If yes, describe _____

Have you received compensation for injuries? _____ If yes, describe _____

EDUCATION

Circle last year completed   Describe any other training or education

Elementary School	5	6	7	8	_____
High School	1	2	3	4	_____
College	1	2	3	4	_____

List below all present and past employment, beginning with your most recent

Name and Address of Company and Type of Business	From Mo.	Yr.	To Mo.	Yr.	Describe in detail the work you did	Weekly Starting Salary	Weekly Last Salary	Reason for Leaving	Name of Supervisor

Name and Address of Company and Type of Business	From Mo.	Yr.	To Mo.	Yr.	Describe in detail the work you did	Weekly Starting Salary	Weekly Last Salary	Reason for Leaving	Name of Supervisor

Name and Address of Company and Type of Business	From Mo.	Yr.	To Mo.	Yr.	Describe in detail the work you did	Weekly Starting Salary	Weekly Last Salary	Reason for Leaving	Name of Supervisor

May we contact the employers listed above? _____ If not, indicate which one(s) you do not wish us to contact. _____

_____

REFERENCES: Give below the names of three persons not related to you that you have known for at least one year.

NAME	ADDRESS	BUSINESS	YEARS ACQUAINTED
1.			
2.			
3.			

The last section of the application is an agreement stating the policies of the company. You are to read this and sign it. This is called, "read the small print."

The facts set forth above in my application for employment are true and complete. I understand that if employed, false statements on this application shall be considered sufficient cause for dismissal. You are hereby authorized to make any investigation of my personal history and financial and credit record through any investigative or credit agencies or bureaus of your choice.

In making this application for employment I also understand that an investigative consumer report may be made whereby information is obtained through personal interviews with my neighbors, friends, or others with whom I am acquainted. This inquiry includes information as to my character, general reputation, personal characteristics, and mode of living. I understand that I have the right to make a written request within a reasonable period of time to receive additional, detailed information about the nature and scope of this investigative consumer report.

_____
Signature of Applicant

APPLICATION FOR EMPLOYMENT

PERSONAL INFORMATION

Date _____

Name _____
             Last   First   Middle

Present Address _____
                Number   Street   City   State   ZIP

Permanent Address _____
                Number   Street   City   State   ZIP

Phone Number _____

Social Security Number _____   Citizen of   Yes
                                           U. S. A.   No

If related to anyone in our employ,
state name and department   _____

EMPLOYMENT DESIRED

Position _____   Date you
                                 can start _____   Salary
Desired _____

Are you employed now? _____   If so, may we inquire of
your present employer? _____

Ever applied to this company before? _____   Where _____   When _____

EDUCATION	Name and Location of School	Years Attended	Date Grad.	Subjects Studied
Elementary School	_____			
High School	_____			
College	_____			
Trade, Business, or Correspondence School	_____			

UNIT 2

You may read about a job in the Help Wanted section of your newspaper that tells you to write to a business or a post office box. This requires a brief, concise letter that lists your qualifications and expresses your interest in the job. Below is a sample copy of a letter answering a Help Wanted advertisement.

127 West Main Street
Lisbon, Ohio 44432
December 22, 1999

Mr. Vincent Morelli
Vito's Italian Kitchen
1021 Bedelia Street
Lisbon, Ohio 44432

Dear Mr. Morelli:

I was interested to read in the Lisbon Sun (12/21/99) about your current need for an evening manager. I have worked in my parents' grocery store (Fred's Stop 'n Shop) since I was ten years old. I am skilled at managing other people, dealing with customers, handling money, and ordering produce and other merchandise.

Though still employed at the grocery store, I would like to gain management experience in a restaurant since I am planning a career in the hospitality industry.

I am 20 years old and in good health. I graduated from Northway High School in 1997 with a 3.1 average. I also have an associate degree in business from Strayer College. I have lived in Lisbon all my life.

Please send me the necessary application or call 555-1234 so an interview can be arranged.

Sincerely,

Albert D. Cunningham
Albert D. Cunningham

ADC

B *Letters of Application:* Write letters seeking employment to two of the following companies. You can use the sample letter on the previous page as a guide. Use the address in the ad for the inside address. Use "Dear Sir or Madam:" for the greeting.

HELP WANTED

OFFICE MANAGER – Must have 5 years office and supervisory experience. 2 weeks paid vacation. Complete medical, dental, and hospitalization plan, pension plan. Salary open. All replies held in strict confidence. Write Richard Co., Box 706, Philadelphia, PA 19255

SALESCLERKS—Full-time or part-time. Market Basket, 1423 Scalp Avenue, Elwell, MI 48832

SERVICE PERSON—

Capable of servicing and repairing oil and gas furnaces. Good pay. Fringe benefits. McCleary Heating, 2451 Bedford St., Dallas, TX 75214

KITCHEN HELP—Wanted

Write The Frog, 207 Radian Dr., Sayre, PA 18840

GENERAL MECHANIC—All-purpose equipment mechanic experienced in gas and diesel engines, electric welding. Steady work. Good pay, vacation, fringe benefits. All replies held confidential. For details reply to *Clifton Gazette*, Box 884, Clifton, SC 29324.

U N I T 2

When you start working, federal law requires you to file a **W-4 form** (Employee's Withholding Exemption Certificate). This form is for all full-time and part-time employees. On this form you should claim all your tax deductions: spouse, children, parents (if you are supporting them), and yourself. Your employer then figures out how much tax to take out, based on your salary and deductions. You will get this form from your employer, usually on your first day of work.

 W-4 Form: Fill out the following form.

Form W-4 (1995)

Want More Money In Your Paycheck?
If you expect to be able to take the earned income credit for 1995 and a child lives with you, you may be able to have part of the credit added to your take-home pay. For details, get Form W-5 from your employer.

Purpose. Complete Form W-4 so that your employer can withhold the correct amount of Federal income tax from your pay.

Exemption From Withholding. Read line 7 of the certificate below to see if you can claim exempt status. *If exempt, complete line 7; but do not complete lines 5 and 6.* No Federal income tax will be withheld from your pay. Your exemption is good for 1 year only. It expires February 15, 1996.

Note: *You cannot claim exemption from withholding if (1) your income exceeds $650 and includes unearned income (e.g., interest*

and dividends) and (2) another person can claim you as a dependent on their tax return.

Basic Instructions. Employees who are not exempt should complete the Personal Allowances Worksheet. Additional worksheets are provided on page 2 for employees to adjust their withholding allowances based on itemized deductions, adjustments to income, or two-earner/two-job situations. Complete all worksheets that apply to your situation. The worksheets will help you figure the number of withholding allowances you are entitled to claim. However, you may claim fewer allowances than this.

Head of Household. Generally, you may claim head of household filing status on your tax return only if you are unmarried and pay more than 50% of the costs of keeping up a home for yourself and your dependent(s) or other qualifying individuals.

Nonwage Income. If you have a large amount of nonwage income, such as interest or dividends, you should consider making

estimated tax payments using Form 1040-ES. Otherwise, you may find that you owe additional tax at the end of the year.

Two Earners/Two Jobs. If you have a working spouse or more than one job, figure the total number of allowances you are entitled to claim on all jobs using worksheets from only one Form W-4. This total should be divided among all jobs. Your withholding will usually be most accurate when all allowances are claimed on the W-4 filed for the highest paying job and zero allowances are claimed for the others.

Check Your Withholding. After your W-4 takes effect, you can use **Pub. 919,** Is My Withholding Correct for 1995?, to see how the dollar amount you are having withheld compares to your estimated total annual tax. We recommend you get Pub. 919 especially if you used the Two Earner/Two Job Worksheet and your earnings exceed $150,000 (Single) or $200,000 (Married). Call 1-800-829-3676 to order Pub. 919. Check your telephone directory for the IRS assistance number for further help.

Personal Allowances Worksheet

A Enter "1" for **yourself** if no one else can claim you as a dependent . . . . **A** _____

B Enter "1" if:
- You are single and have only one job; or
- You are married, have only one job, and your spouse does not work; or
- Your wages from a second job or your spouse's wages (or the total of both) are $1,000 or less.

} . . **B** _____

C Enter "1" for your **spouse.** But, you may choose to enter -0- if you are married and have either a working spouse or more than one job (this may help you avoid having too little tax withheld) . . . . **C** _____

D Enter number of **dependents** (other than your spouse or yourself) you will claim on your tax return . . . . **D** _____

E Enter "1" if you will file as **head of household** on your tax return (see conditions under **Head of Household** above) . **E** _____

F Enter "1" if you have at least $1,500 of **child or dependent care expenses** for which you plan to claim a credit . . **F** _____

G Add lines A through F and enter total here. **Note:** This amount may be different from the number of exemptions you claim on your return ▶ **G** _____

For accuracy, do all worksheets that apply.
- If you plan to **itemize or claim adjustments to income** and want to reduce your withholding, see the Deductions and Adjustments Worksheet on page 2.
- If you are **single** and have **more than one job** and your combined earnings from all jobs exceed $30,000 OR if you are **married** and have a **working spouse or more than one job,** and the combined earnings from all jobs exceed $50,000, see the Two-Earner/Two-Job Worksheet on page 2 if you want to avoid having too little tax withheld.
- If **neither** of the above situations applies, **stop here** and enter the number from line G on line 5 of Form W-4 below.

‑ ‑ ‑ ‑ ‑ **Cut here and give the certificate to your employer. Keep the top portion for your records.** ‑ ‑ ‑ ‑ ‑

Form W-4
Department of the Treasury
Internal Revenue Service

Employee's Withholding Allowance Certificate

▶ **For Privacy Act and Paperwork Reduction Act Notice, see reverse.**

OMB No. 1545-0010

1995

1 Type or print your first name and middle initial	Last name	2 Your social security number

Home address (number and street or rural route)	3 ☐ Single ☐ Married ☐ Married, but withhold at higher Single rate.
	Note: *If married, but legally separated, or spouse is a nonresident alien, check the Single box.*

City or town, state, and ZIP code	4 If your last name differs from that on your social security card, check here and call 1-800-772-1213 for a new card . . . . . . ▶ ☐

5 Total number of allowances you are claiming (from line G above or from the worksheets on page 2 if they apply) . | **5** |

6 Additional amount, if any, you want withheld from each paycheck . . . . | **6** $ |

7 I claim exemption from withholding for 1995 and I certify that I meet **BOTH** of the following conditions for exemption:
- Last year I had a right to a refund of **ALL** Federal income tax withheld because I had **NO** tax liability; **AND**
- This year I expect a refund of **ALL** Federal income tax withheld because I expect to have **NO** tax liability.

If you meet both conditions, enter "EXEMPT" here . . . . ▶ | **7** |

Under penalties of perjury, I certify that I am entitled to the number of withholding allowances claimed on this certificate or entitled to claim exempt status.

Employee's signature ▶

Date ▶ _____ , 19 ___

8 Employer's name and address (Employer: Complete 8 and 10 only if sending to the IRS)	9 Office code (optional)	10 Employer identification number

Cat. No. 10220Q

> **P/T** salesclerk needed **a.s.a.p.** at downtown record shop.
>
> Must be knowledgeable about pop. music & have neat appearance and **gd. attde**.
>
> **Exp. pref.** Pay: $5–6 hr. Hrs.: 5–9 p.m.,3 eves/wk & 9–6 Sat.
>
> Write Mr. Hughes at Box 1021, Austin, TX 73301.
>
> **No ph. calls**, please. **EOE**

 D *Reading an Employment Advertisement:* Read the advertisement for a salesclerk. Answer the questions.

1. What do the boldface words mean?

a. **P/T** _____

b. **a.s.a.p.** _____

c. **gd. attde.** _____

d. **Exp. pref.** _____

e. **No ph. calls** _____

f. **EOE** _____

2. Now, answer the following questions.

a. When is a salesclerk needed? _____

b. What is the salary?_____

c. What should the applicant be familiar with? _____

d. What other qualities should the applicant have?_____

e. Where is the job located?_____

f. When would the job start? _____

The Job Hunt

E *Application Letter:* Complete the following application letter. Circle the best word or phrase out of each group.

November 18, 1999

Mr. Hughes
Box 1021
Austin, Texas 73301

Dear Mr. Hughes:

I was (**excited, thrilled, interested**) by your advertisement in yesterday's paper for a (**person, salesclerk, sales professional**) who (**is an expert with, has heard of, is familiar**) with popular music.

I am a high school senior and would like (**an opportunity to learn new skills; something to do after school until the summer; to make some money like my friends do**).

For references, please call (**my mom and dad; Joey Green, my best friend; Ms. Anne Thomas, my 10th grade biology teacher**). Also, I was employed last summer at High's Dairy as a janitor. I left there because (**I never did get along with my boss; the job lasted only for the summer; I kept asking for a raise and never got one**).

Regarding the hours and pay, (**I would have no trouble working those hours at the salary you advertised; I hope they're negotiable; my parents say they're OK as long as I don't have to work overtime**).

I look forward to (**working for you; hearing from you; stopping by your store to meet with you**).

(**Fondly, Faithfully, Sincerely,**)

(**Charlie Peterson
Charles A. Peterson
C. A. Peterson**)

Imagine that you are visiting a courtroom. What would you expect the judge to look like? What would he or she wear and do? What about the lawyers? What would they look like? Would they appear in suits and carry briefcases?

What would you think if the judge and lawyers wore tennis shoes and jogging suits during court sessions? What would you think if police officers and emergency rescue squads wore sandals and blue jeans while they worked?

Most of us have *expectations*—or beliefs—about how people should look in certain occupations. While none of us wants to judge others by their looks, we all tend to have a clearly defined idea of how others ought to look and behave.

Employers also have a specific belief about how their employees should look and act. This is especially true during a job interview because employers want to know that you understand how to conduct yourself professionally. Even if the job does not require dress clothes, the interview is a special situation. A wise job seeker learns the correct way to look and act for an interview.

 Dressing Successfully for the Interview: As you read through the following list, decide which of the items would be considered proper attire for an interview situation. Write a *P* for "proper" or an *I* for "improper" in the space next to each item.

Men

a. ___ blue jeans	e. ___ open-necked shirt	i. ___ white socks
b. ___ tennis shoes	f. ___ conservative tie	j. ___ silk shirt
c. ___ sports coat	g. ___ dark glasses	k. ___ turtleneck shirt
d. ___ boots	h. ___ leather vest	l. ___ dress shirt

Women

a. ___ some makeup	e. ___ blue jeans	i. ___ turtleneck shirt
b. ___ 4-inch heels	f. ___ pearl necklace	j. ___ 2-piece suit (skirt)
c. ___ tennis shoes	g. ___ large earrings	k. ___ bright red skirt
d. ___ dark sunglasses	h. ___ open-toed shoes	l. ___ conservative scarf

Read these interview "secrets"—guaranteed to give you an edge in the job hunt:

➤ If possible, drive (or walk) by the place where you will be interviewing and decide how much time it will take to travel there. This will prevent lateness.

➤ If you *are* running late, be sure to call ahead to notify the interviewer. This shows that you are considerate of others' time. You may have to reschedule the interview; this is much better than arriving late without an explanation.

➤ Arrive 10–15 minutes early to give yourself time to sit down and relax.

➤ Always bring additional copies of your references and your résumé with you.

➤ Be polite upon arrival; the receptionist often makes comments about job seekers to the employer.

➤ Rehearse your replies to such typical questions as Why do you want to work here? Why did you leave your last job? What are your skills and strengths? What do you know about this company? Do you have reliable transportation? Where do you see yourself five or more years from now? (This last question is especially important because it tells the employer that you have goals.) Also be prepared to ask some of your own questions about the job and the company.

G *Interview Behavior:* The following list represents some things you might do during an interview. Place a *P* next to "proper" behavior or an *I* next to "improper" behavior in the space next to each item.

a. ____ saying "hello" to the receptionist

b. ____ asking about working conditions

c. ____ addressing interviewer by her first name

d. ____ bringing additional references

e. ____ looking the interviewer in the eye

f. ____ asking about the company

g. ____ asking about advancement opportunities

h. ____ leaning on the interviewer's desk

i. ____ shaking hands with the interviewer

j. ____ looking at papers on desk

k. ____ bringing friends along

l. ____ chewing gum

m. ____ asking about benefits

n. ____ eating/drinking

o. ____ looking at your watch

p. ____ smiling

q. ____ asking to use the phone

r. ____ bringing extra résumés

Your first paycheck! It sure looks great, but a good deal of money is taken out for taxes and Social Security. A common reaction is, "But I thought I was getting paid $117.25 a week! What happened?" Well, your total was $117.25 *before deductions.*

		NO. *1170*
	March 6 19 *96*	60-105 / 313

PAY TO THE ORDER OF *James Jones* $ *92.15*

Ninety-two and 15/100 — DOLLARS

AGSNational Bank

MEMO _____ *Jane Ellis*

⑈■ 0 0333 2 ⑈■ ■■ 0 5 2 0 0 0 6 1 8 ⑈■

EARNINGS				DEDUCTIONS							
GROSS PAY	FICA	FEDERAL WH/TAX	STATE INCOME TAX	INSURANCE	CITY TAX	PENSION		TOTAL DEDUCTIONS	NET AMOUNT	PERIOD ENDING
117 25	7 86	9 10	2 87	4 10	1 17			25 10	92 15	2/28

EMPLOYEE'S STATEMENT OF EARNINGS AND DEDUCTIONS.   RETAIN

WORK ASSOCIATES, INC. 90 Cherry Street   Box 519   Memphis, TN 37501

You must pay the following:

➤ **FICA:** This is your payment into Social Security. Total deducted: **$7.86.**

➤ **Withholding Tax:** This money is collected to pay your share of federal income tax. The amount deducted was **$9.10.**

➤ **State Income Tax:** This money pays your share of state tax. The amount deducted: **$2.87.** Some states do not have a state income tax.

➤ **Insurance:** **$4.10** was deducted to pay for your health insurance.

➤ **City Tax:** This **$1.17** pays for the right to live and/or work in the city.

Your total deductions are $25.10.

Let's figure this out: $117.25 Gross pay (total)

$$- \ \underline{25.10} \ \ \text{Deductions}$$

$ 92.15 Net pay (take-home)

In one year, if your salary remains the same, you will earn a gross pay of $6,097. Your take-home pay (after deductions) should be $4,791.80.

When you cash your check, you must sign your name on the back of the check exactly the way it was written on the front. This is called **endorsing** a check. Your signature proves that the check was cashed by you.

Now that you are earning money, you should think about opening both a checking account and a savings account. Call or visit several banks in your town or local area to find the lowest cost of maintaining an account. Some accounts are free of **service charges.** Some are free only if you keep a certain amount of money in the bank. And some banks have service charges for everything.

After you have decided on a bank, you will talk to a person in **new accounts.** You will be given a **signature card** to fill out. The way you sign your name on the card is the way your signature must appear on your checks and other bank forms. This is so no one else will be able to use your checks.

The next thing you should do is put your money into the account, or make a **deposit.** You will be given deposit slips in your checkbook for doing this.

A *Making Deposits:* Fill in your name and address on the blank lines. Then write the date. You want to deposit **$25.35** in cash. Enter **25** in the *dollars* area and **00** in the *cents currency* area. Enter **35** in the *coin* section. Be sure that you enter it in the CASH section since it is cash. Write **$25.35** in the boxes beside the word *Total.*

DEPOSIT TICKET

_____

_____

_____

DATE _____ 19 _____

_____

AGSNational Bank

‖ ■ 0 0333 2 ‖ ■   ■ ■ 0 5 2 0 0 0 6 1 8 ‖ ■

CASH	CURRENCY	25	00
	COIN		35
LIST CHECKS SINGLY			
TOTAL FROM OTHER SIDE			
TOTAL		25	35
LESS CASH RECEIVED			
NET DEPOSIT			

60-105

313

USE OTHER SIDE FOR ADDITIONAL LISTING.

BE SURE EACH ITEM IS PROPERLY ENDORSED

CHECKS AND OTHER ITEMS ARE RECEIVED FOR DEPOSIT SUBJECT TO THE PROVISIONS OF THE UNIFORM COMMERICAL CODE OR ANY APPLICABLE COLLECTION AGREEMENT

Let's try a few more.

Deposit **$10.00** in *cash* and a **$62.87** *check.* Add the two amounts and enter the sum in the total box. Also remember to fill in your name, address, and date.

DEPOSIT TICKET

_____

_____

_____

DATE _____ 19 _____

_____

AGSNational Bank

‖ ■ 0 0333 2 ‖ ■   ■ ■ 0 5 2 0 0 0 6 1 8 ‖ ■

CASH	CURRENCY		
	COIN		
LIST CHECKS SINGLY			
TOTAL FROM OTHER SIDE			
TOTAL			
LESS CASH RECEIVED			
NET DEPOSIT			

60-105

313

USE OTHER SIDE FOR ADDITIONAL LISTING.

BE SURE EACH ITEM IS PROPERLY ENDORSED

CHECKS AND OTHER ITEMS ARE RECEIVED FOR DEPOSIT SUBJECT TO THE PROVISIONS OF THE UNIFORM COMMERICAL CODE OR ANY APPLICABLE COLLECTION AGREEMENT

Deposit a check for **$62.87**. There is no cash in this deposit. Did you write in the total? Did you write in your name and address and the date?

DEPOSIT TICKET

_____
_____
_____

DATE _____ 19 _____

_____

CASH	CURRENCY		
	COIN		
LIST CHECKS SINGLY			
TOTAL FROM OTHER SIDE			
TOTAL			
LESS CASH RECEIVED			
NET DEPOSIT			

60-105
313
USE OTHER SIDE FOR
ADDITIONAL LISTING.

**BE SURE EACH ITEM IS
PROPERLY ENDORSED**

AGSNational Bank

‖■0 0333 2‖■ ■■052000618‖■

CHECKS AND OTHER ITEMS ARE RECEIVED FOR DEPOSIT SUBJECT TO THE PROVISIONS OF THE UNIFORM COMMERICAL CODE OR ANY APPLICABLE COLLECTION AGREEMENT

Next, deposit **$15.50** in cash, a check for **$20.00**, and a check for **$62.87**. Remember to include all other needed information.

DEPOSIT TICKET

_____
_____
_____

DATE _____ 19 _____

_____

CASH	CURRENCY		
	COIN		
LIST CHECKS SINGLY			
TOTAL FROM OTHER SIDE			
TOTAL			
LESS CASH RECEIVED			
NET DEPOSIT			

60-105
313
USE OTHER SIDE FOR
ADDITIONAL LISTING.

**BE SURE EACH ITEM IS
PROPERLY ENDORSED**

AGSNational Bank

‖■0 0333 2‖■ ■■052000618‖■

CHECKS AND OTHER ITEMS ARE RECEIVED FOR DEPOSIT SUBJECT TO THE PROVISIONS OF THE UNIFORM COMMERICAL CODE OR ANY APPLICABLE COLLECTION AGREEMENT

Now that you have deposited money into your checking account, you can begin writing checks. By writing a check, you are taking money out of the bank. Each check must be signed the same way as it appears on the signature card at the bank. You must always write checks in ink so they cannot be changed or erased. On the line "Memo," you can write a note to yourself indicating what the check is for.

You will probably have a preprinted check on which your name and address appear at the top. Also the checks will already be numbered. If necessary, begin by filling in this information. Usually the first thing you write on the check is the *date.* The month can be written out or abbreviated (*July 6, 1996* or *7/6/96*).

The next step is to write the name of the person or business receiving your money. This goes in the space *Pay to the order of.* If you want to write the check to yourself, you only need to write the word *Cash* next to *Pay to the order of.*

B *Writing Checks:* Practice this step. Write out a *Pay to the order of* to three different people.

Pay to the order of _____

Pay to the order of _____

Pay to the order of _____

Next, write in the amount of the check. First, write it in numbers next to the dollar sign ($). Remember that dollars are separated from cents by a decimal point (.).

Then write the amount of money in words. It must be the same amount as numbers. Write Jim Clark a check for $10.50. Write this as follows: *Ten and 50/100*. Always write *dollars* in words and *cents* in numbers over *100*. You do this because there are 100 pennies or cents in a dollar. Also, draw a line after the amount to the word *dollars* on the check. This is so the check cannot be changed.

Practice by writing the following amounts in words and numbers. See the example below.

$13.65   *Thirteen and 65/100* ———————————————————— DOLLARS

$105.72   _____ DOLLARS

$4.09   _____ DOLLARS

If there are no cents, write *00/100* or *no/100*. (Example: $5.00 should be written as *Five and 00/100* or *Five and no/100*.)

Practice by writing the following amounts using a "no/100."

$10.00   *Ten and no/100* ———————————————————— DOLLARS

$18.00   _____ DOLLARS

$20.00   _____ DOLLARS

The last thing to be written on the check is your **signature**. Remember, it must be written the same way at all times.

The following is a sample of a correctly written check.

	NO. 2
	December 9 19 96 $\frac{60\text{-}105}{313}$

PAY TO THE
ORDER OF   *Sam Berger* $ *24.00*

Twenty-four and no/100 ——————————————— DOLLARS

AGSNational Bank

MEMO ——————   *Jane Darr*

‖ ■ 0 0333 2 ‖ ■ ‖ ■ 0 5 2 0 0 0 6 1 8 ‖ ■

C *Check Writing:* Practice writing some checks.

1. Write check number 16 to James Jones for $19.95 for a car part from William Blandy. Make up an address for Blandy.

	NO.
	19 ____ $\frac{60\text{-}105}{313}$

PAY TO THE
ORDER OF   _____ $ _____

_____ DOLLARS

AGSNational Bank

MEMO ——————

‖ ■ 0 0333 2 ‖ ■ ‖ ■ 0 5 2 0 0 0 6 1 8 ‖ ■

2. Write check number 58 to the Hometown Electric Company for $26.60 from Linda Wood for some wire. Make up an address for Wood.

```
_____                          NO. _____
_____
_____            _____ 19 ____    60-105
                                                              ─────
                                                               313
PAY TO THE
ORDER OF    _____    $ _____

_____  DOLLARS

AGSNational Bank
MEMO _____         _____

‖ ▪ 0 0333 2 ‖ ▪   ▪ ▪ 0 5 2 0 0 0 6 1 8 ‖ ▪
```

3. Write check number 33 to Foodmart for $55.09 from Robert Zeller for groceries. Make up an address for Zeller.

```
_____                          NO. _____
_____
_____            _____ 19 ____    60-105
                                                              ─────
                                                               313
PAY TO THE
ORDER OF    _____    $ _____

_____  DOLLARS

AGSNational Bank
MEMO _____         _____

‖ ▪ 0 0333 2 ‖ ▪   ▪ ▪ 0 5 2 0 0 0 6 1 8 ‖ ▪
```

Money and Credit

For each check you write, a **record** must be kept. All checkbooks have a place for records. This part of the checkbook is very important. It tells how much money you have and how much money you have spent. It also tells when and to whom checks were written.

There are two other records to keep. One is the amount of money in your account. This is called the **balance.** The other is a record of **deposits.**

When you write a check, subtract the amount of the check from the old balance to get the new one. This lets you know your present balance at all times.

Example: A $10.50 check was written to Jim Clark on June 11, 1996. It was check number *1*. The check was for baseball tickets. There was a balance of $50.00. There were no deposits. You subtracted the $10.50 check from the $50.00 balance. The new balance is $39.50.

RECORD ALL CHARGES OR CREDITS THAT AFFECT YOUR ACCOUNT

NUMBER	DATE	DESCRIPTION OF TRANSACTION	PAYMENT/DEBIT (-)	✓ T	FEE (IF ANY) (-)	DEPOSIT/CREDIT (+)	BALANCE $	
							50	00
1	6/11	Jim Clark	10 50				10	50
		Baseball Tickets					39	50

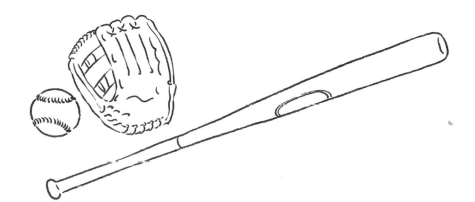

If you have a checking account, you should receive a **bank statement** in the mail every month. This form lets you know how much money you have withdrawn (money you have spent) and how much money you have deposited.

Checks and debits record how many checks you have written and any charges you must pay the bank for your account.

Deposits and credits record the money you have deposited into your account and any money that the bank may have credited to your account.

A bank statement is a form that helps you check your own record with the bank's record of your account.

EAGLE COMMONWEALTH BANK   CHURCHILL, NEW JERSEY   08550

JOE SMITH
874 SMITHIAN STREET
CHURCHILL, NEW JERSEY   08550   2 63

402-779-2
ACCOUNT NO.
06/28/99
STATEMENT DATE

PREVIOUS STATEMENT DATE 05/31/99

BALANCE FROM PREVIOUS STATEMENT	NUMBER OF DEBITS	AMOUNT OF CHECKS & DEBITS	NUMBER OF CREDITS	AMOUNT OF DEPOSITS & CREDITS	STATEMENT BALANCE
132.08	2	132.93	2	42.30	41.45

DATE	CHECKS & DEBITS	CHECKS & DEBITS	DEPOSITS & CREDITS	BALANCE
06/03			34.10 DP	166.18
06/07	32.93			133.25
06/21	100.00		8.20 DP	41.45

CODE SYMBOLS

EC • ERROR CORRECTION   CM • CREDIT MEMO   OD • OVERDRAFT   DP • DEPOSIT
SC • SERVICE CHARGE   DM • DEBIT MEMO   DC • DEPOSIT CORR.   RT • RETURNED CHECK
LS • LISTED CHECKS   IN • OVERDRAFT HANDLING CHARGE

Money and Credit

Now that you are working, you may want to open a **charge account.** This helps to establish a credit rating for yourself. A good credit rating means that you will be able to borrow larger sums of money for a car, a home, or other expensive items. If you do not pay your bills, you will receive a bad credit rating and will have trouble charging anything in the future.

 Completing a Credit Application: Practice filling out some different credit applications. Here are some real applications: one from an oil company, two from a department store, and two for bank credit cards.

APPLICATION FOR OIL COMPANY CREDIT CARD

DO NOT WRITE IN THIS AREA

Full name
First, Middle, Last

Social Security No.

No. of
Dependents

Cycle   Dist.   Acct. No.

Number & Street

Area
Code

Telephone
No.

cc.   Approval   Date

_____ Years _____ Months_____

City & State   ZIP Code   How Long at This Address?   Number of
Credit Cards Desired

Previous Address

☐ Electricity ☐ Fuel Oil ☐ Gas
Which Do You Use to Heat Your Home?

How Long at Years _____ Months_____
Prev. Address

AGE _____ ☐ Single ☐ Divorced ☐ Buying Home ☐ Rent House ☐ Board   Number Owned Cars _____ Trucks_____
☐ Married ☐ Widowed ☐ Own Home ☐ Rent Apt. ☐ Other   How Long at
Present Job?   Years _____ Months_____

Employer (or Armed Service Duty Station)   Type of Business   Position (or Military Rank & Serial No.)

Business Address   Approximate Family Monthly Income

☐ If Less than One Year at Present   Spouse Employed?   Spouse's Employer   Spouse's Position

---

Credit Application
PLEASE PRINT CLEARLY

NAME OF APPLICANT	BIRTH DATE	SOC. SEC. NO.
ADDRESS	CITY, STATE, ZIP CODE	NO. OF DEPENDENTS

HOW LONG AT THIS ADDRESS YRS. MOS.	HOME PHONE	PREVIOUS ADDRESS	CITY, STATE, ZIP CODE

EMPLOYER NAME	POSITION/TITLE	HOW LONG EMPLOYED HERE YRS. MOS.
EMPLOYER ADDRESS	CITY, STATE, ZIP CODE	NET MONTHLY INCOME

BUSINESS PHONE	SELF-EMPLOYED/NATURE OF WORK	OTHER SOURCES OF INCOME

PREVIOUS EMPLOYER (If less than 5 years)	HOW LONG EMPLOYED HERE YRS. MOS.	NET MONTHLY INCOME
PREVIOUS EMPLOYER'S ADDRESS	CITY, STATE, ZIP CODE	POSITION/TITLE

NAME OF CO-APPLICANT	BIRTH DATE	SOC. SEC. NO.
ADDRESS	CITY, STATE, ZIP CODE	HOME PHONE

HOW LONG AT THIS ADDRESS YRS. MOS.	PREVIOUS ADDRESS	CITY, STATE, ZIP CODE

EMPLOYER NAME	POSITION/TITLE	HOW LONG EMPLOYED HERE YRS. MOS.
EMPLOYER ADDRESS	CITY, STATE, ZIP CODE	NET MONTHLY INCOME

BUSINESS PHONE	RELATIONSHIP TO ABOVE APPLICANT

ARE TWO SEPARATE CARDS REQUESTED FOR THIS JOINT ACCT.?

NAME OF NEAREST RELATIVE NOT LIVING WITH YOU	RELATIONSHIP AND ADDRESS	HOME PHONE

YOUR HOME—DO YOU: ☐ OWN   ☐ RENT   ☐ LIVE WITH RELATIVES   ☐ OTHER

LIST ALL CHARGE ACCTS. YOU MAY HAVE

STORE	ACCT. NO.
STORE	ACCT. NO.
STORE	ACCT. NO.

LIST ALL LOANS/MORTGAGES YOU MAY HAVE:

TYPE	ACCT. NO.	AMT. OF MONTHLY PAYMENT
WITH WHAT BANK	ADDRESS	
TYPE	ACCT. NO.	AMT. OF MONTHLY PAYMENT
WITH WHAT BANK	ADDRESS	

ATTACH SEPARATE SHEETS TO LIST ANY ADDITIONAL LOANS, MORTGAGES, OR CHARGE ACCTS.

You are hereby authorized to allow credit to myself or ourselves and family until otherwise notified in writing. Goods purchased to be regarded as necessities and to be paid for out of my or our separate estate. I give the above information for the purpose of obtaining credit concerning any statement made herein.

Applicant Signature	Co-Applicant Signature	Date

APPLICATION TO BE COMPLETED IN NAME OF PERSON IN WHICH THE ACCOUNT IS TO BE CARRIED.

COURTESY TITLES ARE OPTIONAL   PLEASE PRINT

☐ MR.   ☐ MRS.   ☐ MISS   ☐ MS. _____

                                First Name   Initial   Last Name

Mailing Address If Different than Residence Address _____

Residence Address   Street Address   Apt. #   City   State   Zip Code

Phone No: Phone No: Soc. Sec.   Number of

Home _____ Business _____ No. _____ Age ____ Dependents _____
                                                                              (Excluding Applicant)

Are you a United ☐ Yes   If NO, explain

States citizen?   ☐ No   immigration status: _____

How Long at   Own ☐ Rent-Furnished ☐ Rent-Unfurnished ☐ Board ☐ Live With Parents ☐ Monthly Rent or

Present Address _____ Yrs. _____ Mos.   Mortgage Payments $ _____

Name of Landlord or Mortgage Holder   Street Address   City and State

Former Address (If less than 2   How

years at present address) _____ long _____

Employer _____ Street Address _____ City and State _____

How   Net   Monthly ☐

long ____ Yrs. ____ Mos. Occupation: _____ Income $ _____ Weekly ☐
                                                               (Take Home Pay)

Former Employer

(If less than 1 year with present employer) _____ How long _____ Yrs. _____ Mos.

> **ALIMONY, CHILD SUPPORT, OR SEPARATE MAINTENANCE INCOME NEED NOT BE REVEALED IF YOU DO NOT WISH TO HAVE IT CONSIDERED AS A BASIS FOR PAYING THIS OBLIGATION.**
>
> Alimony, child support, separate maintenance received under: Monthly ☐
> ☐ Court order   ☐ Written agreement   ☐ Oral understanding   ☐ Amount $ _____ Weekly ☐

                                Monthly ☐

Other income, if any: Amount $ _____ Weekly ☐   Source _____

                                   Savings ☐   Checking ☐ _____

Name and Address of Bank or Credit Union _____ Acc't No. _____

                                   Savings ☐   Checking ☐ _____

Name and Address of Bank or Credit Union _____ Acc't No. _____

Previous

Sears   ☐ Yes _____ Is Account ☐ Yes Date Final

Account ☐ No   Paid in Full ☐ No Payment Made _____

             At What Sears Store do you usually shop?   Account No.

Relative or Personal

Reference not living

at above address _____

               (Name)   (Street Address)   (City and State)   (Relationship)

CREDIT REFERENCES (Attach additional sheet if necessary.)   List all references (Open or closed within past two years)

Charge Accounts Loan References Bank/Store/Company Address	Date Opened	Name Account Carried in	Account Number	Balance	Monthly Payments

Authorized buyer _____

            First Name   Initial   Last Name   Relationship to applicant

Authorized buyer _____

            First Name   Initial   Last Name   Relationship to applicant

THE INFORMATION BELOW IS REQUIRED IF: (1) YOUR SPOUSE IS AN AUTHORIZED BUYER OR (2) YOU RESIDE IN A COMMUNITY PROPERTY STATE (ARIZONA, CALIFORNIA, IDAHO, LOUISIANA, NEVADA, NEW MEXICO, TEXAS, WASHINGTON) OR (3) YOU ARE RELYING ON THE INCOME OR ASSETS OF ANOTHER PERSON, INCLUDING A SPOUSE OR FORMER SPOUSE, AS A BASIS FOR PAYMENT.

Name of spouse   ☐

Name of former spouse ☐ _____

Name of other person   ☐   Address   Age

                              Street   City

Employer _____ Address _____ and State _____

How long   Soc. Sec.   Net   Monthly ☐

Yrs. ____ Mos. ____   No. _____ Income $ _____ Weekly ☐

                 Occupation   (Take Home Pay)

                                   Savings ☐   Checking ☐ _____

Name and Address of Bank or Credit Union _____ Acc't No. _____

                                   Savings ☐   Checking ☐ _____

Name and Address of Bank or Credit Union _____ Acc't No. _____

                             X _____

                             (Signature of person on whose income or   Date

                                 assets applicant is relying.)

Type of Application ☐ MasterCard/VISA   ☐ MasterCard   ☐ VISA   ☐ Line Increase on   Present
                        Combined Account   Account   Account   Present Account   Account No.

Applicant Information   Please print clearly.

First Name	Middle Initial	Last Name	Social Security No.	Birth Date	Mo.	Day	Year

Present Address	(Street, Apt., City, State, ZIP Code)		Area Code/ Telephone	☐ Own/Buying Home ☐ Rent ☐ Don't Pay for Housing

Previous Address	(Street, Apt., City, State, ZIP Code)		Area Code/ Telephone	Years There

Name of Close Relative Not Living with You	(Street, City, State, ZIP Code)		Area Code/ Telephone	

Present Employer	(Street, City, State, ZIP Code)	Occupation	Area Code/ Telephone	Years There

Previous Employers	(Street, City, State, ZIP Code)	Occupation	Area Code/ Telephone	Years There

Income Information   If self-employed, please provide documentation of net salary or commission per month. Alimony, child support, or separate maintenance income need not be revealed if you do not wish to have it considered as a basis for repaying this obligation.

Monthly Income after Taxes Applicant $	Other Income Per Month Applicant $	Sources of Other Income Applicant	Number of Dependents— include yourself and joint applicant if applicable. ____
Joint Applicant $	Joint Applicant $	Joint Applicant	

Joint Applicant Information   Fill out this section only if you are applying with another person.

First Name	Middle Initial	Last Name	Social Security No.	Birth Date	Mo.	Day	Year

Present Address	(Street, Apt., City, State, ZIP code)		Area Code/ Telephone	Years There

Present Employer	(Street, City, State, ZIP Code)	Occupation	Area Code/ Telephone	Years There

Previous Employers	(Street, City, State, ZIP Code)	Occupation	Area Code/ Telephone	Years There

Debt Information   Please list all outstanding debts, including charge accounts, installment contracts, credit cards, any obligation for which you are a co-maker, child support, alimony, etc. Paid accounts may be used as references. Use a separate sheet if necessary.

Creditor	Type of Debt and Account Number	Names in Which Account Is Carried	Present Balance	Monthly Payment
Landlord/ Mortgage Holder			Rent Not Applicable	$
Car Loan Holder	Year Acct. #		$	$
Average Utility Expenses: Oil, Gas, Electricity			$	$
Additional Credit References			$	$

Other Information   You may use a separate sheet if necessary.

How Many Vehicles Do You Own?	What Year Is Your Oldest Vehicle?		Your Mother's Maiden Name
Checking Acct. No.	Bank/ City, State	Savings Acct. No.	Bank/ City, State

Terms and Signatures

Applicant Signature X	Date	Joint Applicant Signature X	Date

UNITED STATES NATIONAL BANK

APPLICATION FOR:
☐ New Account
  ☐ MasterCard   ☐ VISA
  Credit Limit Desired Each Account
  ☐ $500 ☐ $1,500 ☐ $3,000 ☐ $ _____
    Indicate ☐ Individual Account ☐ Joint Account

☐ Increase Credit Limit Existing Account
☐ MasterCard Account # _____
☐ VISA Account # _____
Total Credit Limit Desired
On Each Account $ _____

APPLICANT SECTION

Last Name	First Name	Initial	Soc. Security No.	Date of Birth

Street Address	City	State	ZIP Code	☐ Own ☐ Rent ☐ Live w/parents	How Long Years Months

Phone No.	Previous Address	City	State	How Long Years Months	No. of Dependents

Present Employer	Position	Business Phone	How Long Years Months	Monthly Salary

Employer's Address	Previous Employer	How Long Years Months

Other Income: Alimony, child or separate maintenance income need not be revealed, if you do not wish to have it considered as a basis for repaying this obligation.

Source	Frequency	Amount $ / $

Name and address of nearest relative (not living with you)	Phone No.	Name of Your Bank ☐ Checking ☐ Savings ☐ Loan

Name and address of mortgage holder or landlord	Obligation Listed in Name of	Balance Owing $	Monthly Payment $

Automobile Make	Year	Financed by and Address		$	$

Other loans, charge accounts, finance co.'s (use additional sheet of paper if necessary) Creditor Name and Address | Account No.

	Account No.		Balance	Payment
1.	#		$	$
2.	#		$	$
3.	#		$	$

MARITAL STATUS (Do not complete if this is an application for an individual account)

Applicant	☐ Married	☐ Separated	☐ Unmarried (including single, divorced, widowed)
Co-Applicant	☐ Married	☐ Separated	☐ Unmarried (including single, divorced, widowed)

CO-APPLICANT SECTION   If this is a joint account, please complete this section.

Co-Applicant's Last Name	First Name	Initial	Soc. Security No.	Date of Birth

Current Address	City	State	ZIP Code

Co-Applicant's Present Employer	Position	Business Phone	How Long Years Months	Monthly Salary $

Employer's Address	Previous Employer	How Long Years Months

SIGNATURES

X _____ ___/___/___   X _____ ___/___/___
Applicant   Date   Co-Applicant   Date

FOR BANK USE ONLY   DO NOT WRITE BELOW THIS LINE

ACCOUNT NUMBER	CY	CREDIT LIMIT	#CARDS	APPROVED BY

After you open a charge account and begin using it, a bill or **statement** will be sent to you. This shows you how much money you owe. You should pay the amount shown on the statement. This amount is usually some portion of the total amount you owe. (Example: if you owe a company a total of $100, your monthly bill may be $20 per month.) If you are able to pay more than the minimum amount shown, you should do so. This will help you reduce the amount of interest you must pay. Always check the bill to make sure that it is correct. Sometimes, a false or wrong charge will occur.

STATEMENT

Zachary Dalton
234 Main Street
Bremen, KS 66412

MINIMUM DUE	NEW BALANCE	AMOUNT PAID
25.00	130.49	

BILLING DATE   7/01

ACCOUNT NO. J987 736 0025D

PLEASE DETACH THIS STUB AND RETURN WITH YOUR PAYMENT

MAIL PAYMENT BY	TO ENSURE IT IS RECEIVED BY	CREDIT LINE	AVAILABLE CREDIT
7/25	8/01	3000.00	2,869.51

BILLING DATE   7/01

ACCOUNT NO. J987 736 0025D

DATE	REFERENCE	CHARGES
6/4	Shirt	$27.95
6/25	Shoes	$52.59
6/30	Pants	$49.95

PREVIOUS BALANCE	CHARGES	PAYMENTS/CREDITS	FINANCE CHARGES	NEW BALANCE
0.00	30.49	0.00	0.00	130.49

ANNUAL PERCENTAGE RATE	PERIODIC RATE	AVERAGE DAILY BALANCE	AMOUNT PAST DUE	MINIMUM DUE INCLUDES AMOUNT PAST DUE
21.6%	1.80%	0.00	0.00	130.49

TO AVOID ADDITIONAL FINANCE CHARGE, PAYMENT OF YOUR NEW BALANCE MUST BE RECEIVED BY: 8/01

Regardless of how much money you earn, you will always want to get the best "deal for your dollar." To do this, you must be careful about where you spend your money and how much you spend. We enjoy a wide range of products in this country. Thousands of businesses spend millions of dollars in advertising to get us to buy their products and services.

As a **consumer**—the person buying these products and services—you have the privilege and obligation to make informed decisions. This means that you must be selective about your choices. The next few pages contain information and activities that will show you how to make smart choices.

Whether you buy something from a catalog or at the store itself, you should be aware of two things: the product's **features** and its **cost**. A product's features may be defined as the *benefits* to the consumer who owns that product. For example, a new shampoo may promote its ability to "add body and bounce to fine, limp hair." A compact disc player may be advertised for "its anti-skip features and its programmability." You must judge if the claims about a product's features are accurate. You must also decide if they matter to you.

Once you have reviewed a product's features and decide to purchase it, you must figure out its cost. Cost may be defined as a *product's total expense* to you. A product's cost is often more than just the numbers you read on a price tag or in a catalog. Often, a product comes with **hidden** or **extra costs.** For example, a certain new car may be advertised for $28,000, but you must add the cost of fuel, maintenance, and insurance. Cars, in particular, vary widely in these costs. A sports car, for instance, is usually more expensive to insure than other cars. Also, cars with good fuel economy will take less gasoline and will cost less to run. In addition, a well-made automobile may last twice as long as one made with less care.

Also, find out as much as you can about what others say about a product. The magazine *Consumer Reports* is a well-known source of information about all sorts of merchandise. Your local library can supply you with other information, including lists of manufacturers and buying guides. Finally, keep in mind that most products come with guarantees or warranties. Find out what each one includes and do not hesitate to hold a company to its promises.

Shopping

A *Comparison Shopping:* For this activity, you will need a recent Sunday edition of your local newspaper. (It usually contains the most advertisements.) Choose one of the following items: car, videocassette recorder, luggage set, jogging shoes, 19" color television, computer system. Cut out two advertisements for this item and paste them in the boxes below. Then answer the questions.

Item A

Item B

1. List the name and make of each item. *Example:* Pressler VCR 224

   Item A: _____   Item B: _____

2. What are the special features of each item?

   Item A: _____   Item B: _____

   _____   _____

   _____   _____

3. Circle the features that matter most to you. *Example:* automatic shift, easy financing, choice of colors, remote control.

4. Price of each item. A: _____   B: _____

5. List any special terms of payment. *Example:* 18–month financing, at 10.5%

   A: _____

   B: _____

6. How will you pay for the item? If paying by credit card, assume that the annual percentage rate is 18%. Add 18% of the cost of the item to its advertised price. What is the "real" price of the item? _____

7. Based on your answers, which item is the best buy for you?

   _____

Catalog shopping (or direct mail shopping) is becoming a popular way to shop. It is convenient because you never have to leave your home. A catalog of merchandise is sent to your home, you make selections, and then you mail back your order with your payment. Within a few weeks, the merchandise is delivered right to your door.

 Catalog Shopping: Order a cookset from this catalog.

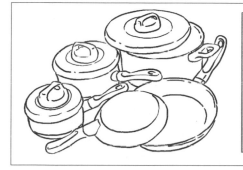

Stainless Steel Cookset

Compact, light in weight cookset works well with the Apex I and other camp stoves. Nesting stainless steel pans have copper bottoms for fast, even heat distribution. 2 qt., $1\frac{1}{2}$ qt. saucepans with covers. Top cover is a $6\frac{1}{2}$" fry pan. Carry bag. Made in Korea.

7700PP Stainless Steel Cookset, $17.50 ppd.

ORDERED BY: Phone ( ) _____ ❑ Day ❑ Night

If name or address is incorrect please print correct information.

GIFT ORDER or SHIP TO: Please print. Use only if different from "Ordered by."

❑ Mr.
❑ Mrs.
❑ Ms.

Street/Route   Box/Apt.

City   State   ZIP

Gift Card-From

Federal Express Recipient Phone No. ( ) _____

If a peel-off label is available on the back cover, attach it here.

Page	Stock No.	Color	Size	Inseam	How Many	Description	Total Amount

If you need more space, please attach a separate sheet of paper.

PAYMENT METHOD

❑ MasterCard ❑ VISA ❑ Check or Money Order (Please, no currency)

❑ American Express   Amount Enclosed $ _____

Card Account Number _____

Expiration Date Required   Customer Signature

Month _____ Year _____ _____

Item Total		
5% Sales Tax on Items Delivered in Maine		
FREE regular SHIPPING & HANDLING within U.S.		
Optional FEDERAL EXPRESS (See reverse side)		
SPECIAL SHIPMENT or Foreign Shipment (see reverse side)		
"Thank you for your order" **TOTAL**		

UNIT 4

C *Ordering:* Practice filling out the order form. Order a first aid pouch from this catalog.

First Aid Pouches

Professional quality first aid kits with specially sized pockets that hold needed first aid equipment. Manufactured from 8 oz. nylon pack cloth that has been coated for water resistance. Made in U.S.A. Three styles: "Mini" Kit. "Basic" Kit. "Standard" Kit. Color: Red.

"Mini" First Aid Pouch. For everyday, minor injuries. Includes $\frac{1}{2}$" adhesive tape, 2 sterile gauze pads, 6–$\frac{3}{4}$" adhesive bandages, 2 knuckle bandages, 2 finger bandages, 1–3" x 4" moleskin, 4 antibacterial towelettes, 2 antibiotic ointment packets, needle, razor blade, and 12 aspirin. Measures 5" x 7". Wt. 4 oz.

6098KE "Mini" First Aid Pouch, $6.95 ppd.

"Basic" First Aid Pouch. Good choice for bicycling, fishing, day hiking, or cross-country ski trips. Includes 6–1" x 3" adhesive bandages, 2–4" x 4" gauze pads, 2–3" x 4" adhesive pads, 1–4" bandage compress, 1–5 yd. roll of 1" gauze, 1 porous 1" adhesive tape roll, 1–3" x 4" moleskin, 1 needle, 1 razor blade, 4 antibacterial towelettes, 1 zip-top plastic bag, 4 pill vials, and 1 first aid information booklet. Measures 1" x 4" x 5". Wt. 8 oz.

6127KE "Basic" First Aid Pouch, $18.50 ppd.

"Standard" First Aid Pouch. For larger groups or individuals who travel more than a few hours from civilization. Includes 12–1" x 3" adhesive bandages, 6 butterfly bandages, 6–4" x 4" gauze pads, 1–4" bandage compress, 2–5 yd. rolls of 2" gauze, 1 porous 2" wide adhesive tape, 2–3" x 4" moleskins, 1–40" triangular bandage, 1 wire mesh splint, 1 thermometer, 1 pair of tweezers, 1 needle, 1 razor blade, 1 oz. antibacterial soap, 12 oz. Tincture of Benzoin, 12 five-grain aspirin, 6 antacid tablets. 1 zip-top plastic bag, 4 pill vials, 1 accident report form, and 1 first aid information booklet. Pouch measures 1$\frac{1}{2}$" x 5" x 10". Weight 21 oz.

6128KE "Standard" First Aid Pouch, $48.50 ppd.

ORDERED BY: Phone (   ) _____ ❑ Day ❑ Night
If name or address is incorrect please print correct information.

If a peel-off label is available on the back cover, attach it here.

GIFT ORDER or SHIP TO: Please print. Use only if different from "Ordered by."

❑ Mr.
❑ Mrs.
❑ Ms.

Street/Route   Box/Apt.

City   State   ZIP

Gift Card-From

Federal Express Recipient Phone No. (   ) _____

Page	Stock No.	Color	Size	Inseam	How Many	Description	Total Amount
					If you need more space, please attach a separate sheet of paper.	

PAYMENT METHOD

❑ MasterCard ❑ VISA ❑ Check or Money Order (Please, no currency)

❑ American Express   Amount Enclosed $ _____

Card Account Number _____
Expiration Date Required   Customer Signature

Month _____ Year _____   _____

Item Total	
5% Sales Tax on Items Delivered in Maine	
FREE regular SHIPPING & HANDLING within U.S.	
Optional FEDERAL EXPRESS (See reverse side)	
SPECIAL SHIPMENT or Foreign Shipment (see reverse side)	
"Thank you for your order" **TOTAL**	

Test Units 1–4

Abbreviations in Applications and Ads

A Write the letter of the word or phrase that shows what each abbreviation means.

a. hour	d. number	g. year	j. inches	m. male
b. week	e. female	h. street	k. month	n. account
c. evening	f. part time	i. as soon as possible	l. Saturday	o. experience

_____ **1.** in.

_____ **2.** no.

_____ **3.** M

_____ **4.** hr.

_____ **5.** St.

_____ **6.** a.s.a.p.

_____ **7.** Sat.

_____ **8.** eve.

_____ **9.** wk.

_____ **10.** F

_____ **11.** mo.

_____ **12.** yr.

_____ **13.** acct.

_____ **14.** PT

_____ **15.** exp.

Interview Skills

B Write *Yes* or *No* to answer each question.

_____ **1.** Is it a good idea to call the person interviewing you by his or her first name?

_____ **2.** Should you bring extra copies of your résumé and your references?

_____ **3.** Would a turtleneck sweater be something appropriate for a man to wear to an interview?

_____ **4.** Should a woman wear long, dangling earrings?

_____ **5.** Are tennis shoes a good choice for both men and women to wear to an interview?

_____ **6.** Should you avoid asking questions about the company and the job?

_____ **7.** Would it be okay to bring a friend with you for moral support?

_____ **8.** Is it a good idea to say "Hello" to the receptionist?

_____ **9.** If you are going to be late, should you call and notify the interviewer?

_____ **10.** If it relaxes you, is it all right to chew gum?

Deposit Ticket

C Fill in the following deposit ticket with all the information needed to make this deposit.

your name and address, today's date, $22.50 in cash, a check for $83.77

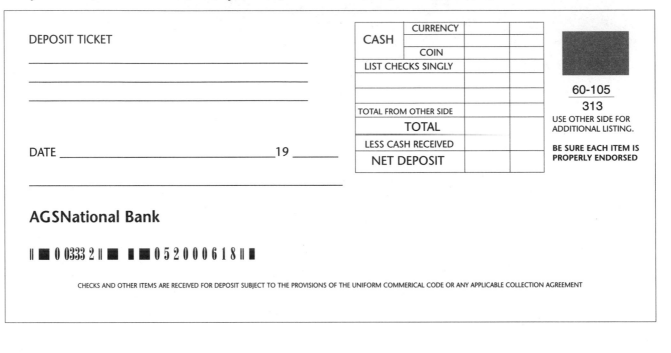

Writing a Check

D Complete the check that follows, using the information given.

The check is for State Power and Light to pay an electric bill of Hector Gonzalez of 1212 Mesa View, Del Rio, Texas, 78840. The check number is 152, and the check was written on March 28 of this year and is for $82.53.

Getting There

Traveling is one of the most popular ways of spending leisure time. While some people want to see foreign countries, others find adventure in their own states and towns. We all tend to take our hometowns for granted, but alert adventurers will find things to do in their "own backyard."

A bus is a nice way to travel. It is comfortable, it is inexpensive, and it can help you see a great deal of the country up close. Sometimes, the most difficult part of a bus trip is reading the bus schedule. You have to read up, down, right, and left. You have to translate the codes and decide which bus is best for you. A train schedule and an airline schedule are also included in this section. They can also be difficult to understand. Be sure to check with the bus company, train company, or airline when making plans.

Bus and air travel are the two most common forms of public transportation in our country. Train travel is another option, but not as many areas are served by train lines. Travel agencies can usually provide you with a number of choices since they have access to the most current information about special fares and reduced rates for travelers.

Getting There

Just about everyone wants to get a driver's license and car as soon as possible. The ability to drive opens up many new opportunities and provides you with more freedom than you might have had before. A car is also a great time-saver.

To obtain a driver's license, you must be of proper age and fill out an application similar to the one that follows.

 Practice filling out this application.

APPLICATION FOR A DRIVER'S LICENSE

Print in Ink

FULL NAME _____   _____
           (last name)   (first name)   (middle name)   Social Security #

MAILING ADDRESS: _____
                  Number and Street   City   State   ZIP Code

EYES _____   HAIR _____   WEIGHT _____   HEIGHT _____

EMPLOYER _____   OCCUPATION _____

THESE QUESTIONS MUST BE ANSWERED by placing an X in the space under the words NO and YES. If you answer YES, details must be given in the space provided.

      NO   YES

1. _____ _____ Have you ever held a driver's license? When last? _____

2. _____ _____ Have you ever been examined for a driver's license? Did you pass? _____

3. _____ _____ Have you ever held a license in any other state? Where? _____

4. _____ _____ Have you ever been denied a license? Why? _____

5. _____ _____ Has your driving privilege ever been revoked, suspended, or canceled?
                How many times? _____ When? _____ Where? _____

6. _____ _____ Have you ever been convicted of any traffic violations? How many times? _____

7. _____ _____ Have you ever been a driver in a motor vehicle accident? How many times? _____

8. _____ _____ Have you ever been subject to losses of consciousness or muscular control? _____

9. _____ _____ Have you ever been addicted to the use of alcohol or narcotics? Are you cured? _____

10. _____ _____ Do you have any physical or mental defects? What are they? _____

I do solemnly swear that I am the person named and described herein and that the statements on this application are true and correct.

SIGNATURE: _____   Date: _____

Now that you are working and have a driver's license, you may decide to buy a car. This is a very big step.

 The following form is a Bill of Sale for a motor vehicle. Review and practice filling this out. It will help you understand what is involved in buying a car.

Bill of Sale of Motor Vehicle

STATE OF _____)

) SS:

COUNTY OF _____)

KNOW YE ALL PEOPLE BY THESE PRESENTS,

That I/We, _____ , of

_____ ,

   Street Address   *City*   *State*   *ZIP*

and _____ , of

_____ ,

   Street Address   *City*   *State*   *ZIP*

for and in consideration of payment of the sum of $ _____ , the receipt of which is hereby acknowledged, do hereby grant, bargain, sell and convey to:

_____ , of

_____ ,

   Street Address   *City*   *State*   *ZIP*

and _____ , of

_____ ,

   Street Address   *City*   *State*   *ZIP*

and his/her/their heirs, executors, administrators, successors and assigns the following motor vehicle:

_____

Year   *Make*   *Model*   *Serial No.*   *Engine No.*

Said vehicle is sold to the buyer(s) with current (State) (County) (Municipal) inspection sticker and current (State) (County) (Municipal) tax sticker and a total mileage of _____ , with no other warranties or representations expressed or implied.

I/We hereby represent that I/we are the lawful owner(s) of said vehicle and that I/we have full legal right, power, and authority to sell said vehicle. I/We further warrant said vehicle to be free from all encumbrances and that I/we will warrant and defend said vehicle hereby sold against any and all persons whomsoever.

    IN WITNESS WHEREOF, I/we, the seller(s), have hereto set my/our hand and seal this _____ day of _____ , 19 _____ .

                  (Signed) _____

                                    Seller

                  (Signed) _____

                                      Seller

Odometer statements verify the mileage of a used car upon its sale. This document is important because the number of miles an automobile has been driven greatly affects its value and, therefore, its price.

C Practice filling out this form. It continues on the next page.

Buyer's Acceptance

I/We, _____ and _____ , buyer(s) of said vehicle, hereby accept the above-described vehicle in good order and repair pursuant to the herein before BILL OF SALE this _____ day of _____ , 19 ____.

(Signed) _____
Buyer

(Signed) _____
Buyer

Odometer Mileage Statement

I, _____ , state that the odometer of the vehicle described below now reads _____ miles/kilometers.

Check one box only.
- ❏ 1. I hereby certify that to the best of my knowledge the odometer reading as stated above reflects the actual mileage of the vehicle described below.

- ❏ 2. I hereby certify that to the best of my knowledge the odometer reading as stated above reflects the amount of mileage in excess of the designed mechanical odometer limit of 999,999 miles/kilometers of the vehicle described below.

- ❏ 3. I hereby certify that to the best of my knowledge the odometer reading as stated above is NOT the actual mileage of the vehicle described below and should not be relied upon.

Make	*Model*	*Body Type*
Year	*Vehicle Identification No.*	*Last Plate No.*

Check one box only.

❑ 1. I hereby certify that the odometer of said vehicle was not altered, set back, or disconnected while in my possession, and I have no knowledge of anyone else doing so.

❑ 2. I hereby certify that the odometer was altered for repair or replacement purposes while in my possession and that the mileage registered on the repaired or replacement odometer was identical to that before such service.

❑ 3. I hereby certify that the repaired or replacement odometer was incapable of registering the same mileage, that it was reset to zero, and that the mileage on the original odometer or the odometer before repair was _____ miles/kilometers.

Transferor's (Seller's) Address:

_____
Street Address   *City*   *State*   *ZIP*

Transferor's Signature _____ Date of Statement _____

Transferee's (Buyer's) Name _____

_____
Street Address   *City*   *State*   *ZIP*

Receipt of Copy Acknowledged   (Signed) _____
                                                    Transferee/Buyer

Getting There

Whether you are driving, biking, or walking, learning how to read a road map is essential to getting around by yourself. To use the map shown here, look first at the **legend** (the box in the lower right-hand corner) to see what all the markings mean. Notice that the symbols show, among other things, types of **roads;** locations of important landmarks, such as **parks, schools,** and **churches;** and special information that advises you about roads or rapid transit lines **under construction.** Also notice the **compass marker** in the upper right-hand corner of the map.

Use this information to answer the questions on the following page.

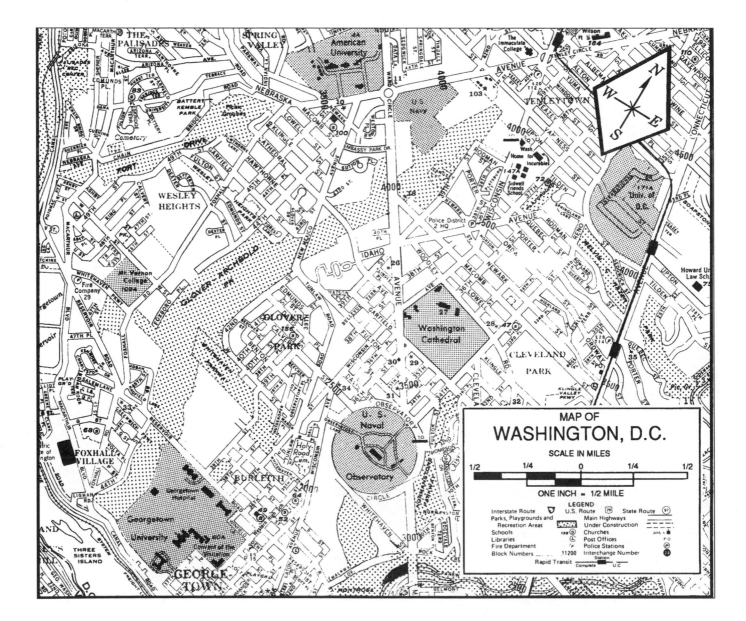

D *Understanding Maps:* Answer the following questions about the map on the opposite page. Choose the correct answer for each question and write the letter in the space provided.

_____ 1. Find the Washington Cathedral. Where is it located in relation to the U.S. Naval Observatory?
   a. northwest
   b. northeast
   c. southeast

_____ 2. Find the University of D.C. Which of the following streets runs into it?
   a. Nebraska Avenue
   b. Van Ness Street
   c. Newark Street

_____ 3. What park is east of the Washington Cathedral?
   a. Glover Park
   b. Cleveland Park
   c. Montrose Park

_____ 4. Which of these schools is located the farthest north on the map?
   a. American University
   b. Mt. Vernon College
   c. Georgetown University

_____ 5. What does [   ] refer to?
   a. schools
   b. construction
   c. parks

_____ 6. What street is north of Georgetown University?
   a. Reservoir Road
   b. 44th Street
   c. Canal Road

_____ 7. On this map, one inch equals what distance?
   a. one mile
   b. one acre
   c. one half of a mile

_____ 8. What street is just south of American University?
   a. Arizona Avenue
   b. Van Ness Street
   c. Nebraska Avenue

E *Plan a Short Trip Within a City:* Using the map and instructions below, answer the questions on the following page.

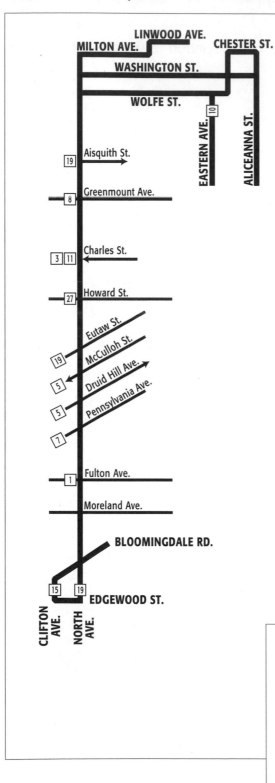

Monday Through Friday

TO CANTON					TO WALBROOK JUNCTION				
NORTH & EDGEWOOD	NORTH & CHARLES	NORTH & GREENMOUNT	WASHINGTON & ALICEANNA	CANTON	CANTON	WASHINGTON & ALICEANNA	NORTH & GREENMOUNT	NORTH & CHARLES	NORTH & EDGEWOOD
MID-DAY SERVICE					MID-DAY SERVICE				
845	907	911	930	-	836	-	906	910	934
857	916	920	-	948	-	854	916	920	944
907	926	930	949	-	857	-	926	930	954
909	928	932	-	-	-	920	941	945	1009
921	940	944	-	1012	929	-	957	1001	1025
935	954	958	1017	-	-	953	1013	1017	1041
940	959	1003	-	-	959	-	1027	1031	1055
951	1010	1014	-	1042	-	1021	1041	1045	1109
1005	1024	1028	1047	-	-	-	1048	1052	1116
1019	1038	1042	-	1110	1028	-	1056	1100	1124
1032	1051	1055	1114	-	-	1051	1111	1115	1139
1047	1106	1110	-	1138	1056	-	1125	1129	1153
1101	1120	1124	1143	-	-	1115	1134	1138	1202
1113	1132	1136	-	1205	1115	-	1145	1149	1213
1124	1143	1147	1207	-	-	1135	1155	1159	1223
1135	1154	1158	-	1227	1134	-	1204	1208	1232
1146	1205	1209	1229	-	-	1154	1214	1218	1242
1156	1216	1220	-	1249	1154	-	1224	1228	1252
1206	1226	1230	1250	-	-	1214	1234	1238	102
1216	1236	1240	-	109	1214	-	1244	1248	112
1226	1246	1250	110	-	-	1234	1254	1258	122
1236	1256	100	-	129	1234	-	104	108	132
1246	106	110	130	-	-	1254	114	118	142
1256	116	120	-	149	1254	-	124	128	152
107	127	131	151	-	-	114	134	138	202
116	136	140	-	209	114	-	144	148	212
126	146	150	210	-	-	134	154	158	222
136	156	200	-	229	133	-	204	208	232
146	206	210	230	-	-	154	214	218	243
156	217	221	-	250	151	-	222	226	252
206	227	231	251	-	-	209	230	234	300
216	237	241	-	313D	205	-	237	241	325E
226	247	251	311		B230	-	242	246	312

HOW TO USE THIS TABLE: When do you want to be there? Look at the timetable *under your destination* and see which time is closest to the time you want to be there. Then look to the left and see what time you should take that bus at your boarding point.

☐ represents transfer points.

----- indicates early morning, late evening service

1. If you live at the corner of Washington Street and Aliceanna Street and want to visit a friend who lives at the intersection of North Avenue and Edgewood Street, what time would you have to leave your nearest bus stop to arrive there at these times?

   a. 10:41 A.M. _____

   b. 12:23 P.M. _____

   c. 1:45 P.M. _____

   d. 3:15 P.M. _____

2. Your nearest bus stop is North and Edgewood. You are traveling to North and Greenmount, but have missed the 9:21 bus. When is the next bus due to arrive?

   _____

3. If you start at Moreland Avenue and head for Linwood Avenue, what should be the next stop after Charles Street?

   _____

4. What days does this bus schedule cover?

   _____

5. What does a number inside a box represent? _____

6. a. What does a broken line indicate? _____

   b. Can you find any broken lines on this map? _____

7. What number is found on these transfer points?

   a. Howard Street _____

   b. Greenmount Avenue _____

   c. Pennsylvania Avenue _____

   d. Eastern Avenue _____

8. How many transfer points are there between Fulton Avenue and Eutaw Street?

   _____

9. If you want to reach Canton from North Avenue and Charles Street, what time would you have to leave to arrive at these times?

   a. 10:15 A.M. _____

   b. 1:00 P.M. _____

   c. 1:45 P.M. _____

   d. 10:00 A.M. _____

Sample Bus Schedule

	Schedule for		
	PHILADELPHIA • HARRISBURG • LANCASTER • WINCHESTER		
Bus Number	Destination/Time	Originating City/Time	Notes
39	Phila. 1:10 P.M.	Lanc. 7:20 A.M.	D
66	Harris. 2:15 P.M.	Winch. 10:30 A.M.	W
58	Winch. 4:30 P.M.	Phila. 12:05 P.M.	SS
91	Lanc. 8:00 P.M.	Phila. 4:40 P.M.	SP
15	Phila. 10:50 P.M.	Winch. 7:30 P.M.	E
17	Harris. 3:45 P.M.	Lanc. 11:30 A.M.	SS
88	Winch. 7:45 P.M.	Harris. 3:35 P.M.	D
37	Lanc. 5:30 P.M.	Phila. 1:00 P.M.	W

Key to Notes:

W = Weekdays only   SP = Special (Wednesdays and Fridays only)
D = Daily   SS = Saturdays and Sundays only
E = Evenings only

F *Plan a City-to-City Bus Trip:* Plan a round-trip bus ride for the cities listed below. Use the schedule on the previous page to answer each question.

1. Philadelphia to Lancaster

   a. On what days can you take a bus from Philadelphia to Lancaster?

   _____

   b. What time will your bus leave Philadelphia?

   _____

   c. What are the numbers of the two buses that you could take for your trip?

   _____

2. Harrisburg to Winchester

   a. On what days can you take a bus from Harrisburg to Winchester?

   _____

   b. What time will your bus arrive in Winchester?

   _____

3. What do these symbols mean?

   a. SS _____

   b. W _____

   c. E _____

   d. SP _____

Sample Train Schedule

READ DOWN						READ UP	
41	47			Train Number		40	46
Broad-way Limited	The Pennsyl-vanian			Train Name		Broad-way Limited	The Pennsyl-vanian
Daily	Daily			Frequency of Operation		Daily	Daily
R ✦				Type of Service		R ✦	
		km	Mi				
215P	730A	0	0	Dp New York, NY-Penn. Sta. (ET)	Ar	119P	637P
R229P	743A	16	9	Newark, NJ-Penn. Sta.		D104P	D623P
	759A	37	23	Metropark, NJ-Iselin			609P
	810A	51	32	New Brunswick, NJ			559P
	825A	76	47	Princeton Jct., NJ (Princeton)			543P
R312P	837A	94	57	Trenton, NJ		D1219P	533P
	900A	136	85	North Philadelphia, PA			509P
R345P	910A	145	90	Ar Philadelphia, PA-30th St. Sta.	Dp	D1147A	500P
R405P	925A	145	90	Dp	Ar	D1123A	444P
	936A	156	97	Ardmore, PA •			430P
R430P	950A	176	109	Paoli, PA		D1056A	416P
	1002A	195	121	Downingtown, PA			403P
511P	1032A	253	157	Lancaster, PA		1015A	333P
548P	1103A	311	193	Ar Harrisburg, PA (State College)	Dp	942A	300P
558P	1103A	311	193	Dp Harrisburg, PA (State College)	Ar	937A	300P
704P	1210P	409	254	Lewistown, PA •		823A	147P
743P	1248P	467	291	Huntingdon, PA •		743A	109P
	118P	499	311	Tyrone, PA •			1242P
826P	136P	521	325	Altoona, PA		655A	1221P
930P	240P	584	364	Johnstown, PA		554A	1121A
	327P	644	401	Latrobe, PA •			1036A
1024P	334P	660	411	Greensburg, PA •		450A	1025A
1110P	418P	710	442	Ar Pittsburgh, PA-Main Sta.	Dp	403A	945A
1140P		710	442	Dp	Ar	333A	
144A		874	544	Canton, OH		108A	
339A		1014	631	Crestline, OH •		1130P	
501A		1130	702	Lima, OH		952P	
619A		1225	762	Fort Wayne, IN (ET)		845P	
731A		1393	866	Valparaiso, IN (CT)		545P	
801A		1423	885	Gary, IN-5th & Chase Sts. •		524P	
816A		1429	894	Hammond/Whiting, IN		514P	
851A		1463	910	Ar Chicago, IL-Union Sta. (CT)	Dp	450P	

Services

➤ The Broadway Limited   *New York—Chicago*
➤ The Pennsylvanian   *New York—Pittsburgh*

Reference Marks

R All reserved train
✦ Complete meals and snacks
• Tickets not available at station
D Stops only to discharge passengers

G *Reading a Train Schedule:* Use the train schedule on the previous page to plan the following trips.

1. Plan a trip from Philadelphia, PA, to Pittsburgh, PA.

   a. Departure time from Philadelphia _____

   b. Arrival time in Pittsburgh _____

   c. How many miles will you travel? _____

2. Plan a trip from Newark, NJ, to Harrisburg, PA.

   a. Departure time from Newark _____

   b. Arrival time in Harrisburg _____

   c. How many miles will you travel? _____

3. Plan a trip from New York, NY, to Chicago, IL.

   a. Departure time from New York _____

   b. Arrival time in Chicago _____

   c. How many miles will you travel? _____

4. What do these symbols mean?

   a. $\boxed{R}$ _____

   b. • _____

   c. D _____

U N I T 5

Sample Airline Schedule   Pennsylvania Airlines

HARRISBURG/YORK/HERSHEY
Reservations 800–555–4253   Cargo 717–555–9426

TO					FROM				
Leave	Arrive	Freq	Flight	Stops	Leave	Arrive	Freq	Flight	Stops
Washington					**Washington**				
7:05A	7:50A		1216	0	8:20A	9:00A		1216	0
9:15A	10:00A		1227	0	10:15A	11:00A		1227	0
11:25A	12:10A		1210	0	1:00P	1:45P		1210	0
1:15P	1:59P		1221	0	3:15P	4:00P		1221	0
4:45P	5:30P		1255	0	5:59P	6:45P		1256	0
7:00P	7:45P	Ex Sa	1224	0	9:29P	10:15P	Ex Sa	1215	0
John F. Kennedy					**John F. Kennedy**				
7:00A	8:45A		1200	1	9:15A	11:00A	Ex Su	1201	1
8:35A	9:45A	(Eff 12/15)	1252	0					
8:40A	9:50A	(Disc 12/15)	1252	0	10:05A	11:20A	Ex Sa Su	1253	0
9:15A	10:59A	Ex Sa Su	1218	1	11:15A	1:00P	Ex Sa	1219	1
11:15A	1:00P		1202	1	5:30P	6:40P	Sa only	1217	0
3:00P	4:10P		1211	0	8:00P	9:10P	Ex Sa	1207	0
5:15P	7:00P		1222/1212	1	8:15P	10:15P		1223	1
LaGuardia					**LaGuardia**				
7:30A	8:40A	Ex Sa Su	1208	0	8:55A	10:10A	Ex Sa Su	1208	0
2:10P	3:25P	Ex Sa	1228	0	3:50P	4:55P	Ex Sa	1228	0
5:15P	6:30P	Ex Sa	1229	0	6:45P	8:00P	Ex Sa	1229	0
Philadelphia					**Philadelphia**				
7:00A	745A		1200	0	10:15A	11:00A	Ex Su	1201	0
9:15A	9:59A	Ex Sa Su	1218	0	12:20P	1:00P	Ex Sa	1219	0
11:15A	11:59A		1202	0	1:45P	2:30P		1259	0
12:45P	1:30P		1259	0	3:45P	4:30P		1261	0
2:45P	3:30P		1260	0	6:15P	7:00P	(Disc 12/15)	1262	0
5:05P	5:50P	(Eff 12/15)	1222	0	6:25P	7:10P	(Eff 12/15)	1262	0
5:15P	6:00P	(Disc 12.15)	1222	0	9:30P	10:15P		1223	0
State College					**State College**				
11:40A	12:15P	Ex Sa	1253	0	7:50A	8:25A	(Eff 12/15)	1252	0
					7:55A	8:30A	(Disc 12/15)	1252	0
7:20P	8:00P	Ex Sa Su	1262	0	4:20P	4:55P	Ex Sa	1222	0

JOHNSTOWN
Reservations 814–555–6704   Cargo 814–555–3510

TO					FROM				
Leave	Arrive	Freq	Flight	Stops	Leave	Arrive	Freq	Flight	Stops
Pittsburgh					**Pittsburgh**				
7:10A	7:50A	(Eff 12/15)	1246	0					
7:20A	8:00A	(Disc 12/15)	1246	0	9:30A	10:50A	Sa only	1263	1
10:50A	11:30A	Ex Sa	1247	0	9:40A	10:20A	Ex Sa	1247	0
11:05A	11:45A	Sa Only	1263	0	12:40P	1:55P	Sa Only	1242	1
2:05P	3:00P	Sa Only	1242	0	1:45P	2:25P	Ex Sa	1248	0
3:20P	4:00P	Ex Sa	1248	0	3:05P	4:20P	Sa Only	1265	1
4:30P	5:10P	Sa Only	1265	0	5:00P	6:10P	Ex Sa	1249	1
6:20P	6:59P	(Eff 12/15)	1249	0					
6:20P	7:00P	(Disc 12/15)	1249	0	5:30P	6:10P	Sa Only	1266	0
8:25P	9:05P	Ex Sa	1250	0	7:35P	8:15P	Ex Sa	1250	0
					10:30P	11:10P	Ex Sa	1251	0

H *Reading an Airline Schedule:* Use the airline schedule on the previous page to plan the following trips.

1. Plan a trip from State College to Harrisburg.

   a. Flight number _____

   b. Departure time from State College _____

   c. Arrival time in Harrisburg _____

2. Plan a trip from Philadelphia to Harrisburg.

   a. Flight number _____

   b. Departure time from Philadelphia _____

   c. Arrival time in Harrisburg _____

3. Plan a trip from Johnstown to Pittsburgh.

   a. Flight number _____

   b. Departure time from Johnstown _____

   c. Arrival time in Pittsburgh _____

4. Plan a trip from New York City (John F. Kennedy Airport) to Harrisburg.

   a. Flight number _____

   b. Departure time from New York City _____

   c. Arrival time in Harrisburg _____

Getting There

New drivers soon see that the road has a language of its own. Road signs are a universal—or generic—language of symbols. These symbols are used around the world and help direct people traveling both here and in foreign countries.

Signs are helpful in several ways. They tell you where to find services (like hotels, restaurants, phones, and fuel), warn you about road conditions, and give you directions. Here are some sample signs and their meanings:

Regulatory Signs
(Red on white)

1. Yield
2. Do Not Enter
3. No Right Turn
4. No U-Turn
5. No Trucks
6. No Bicycles

Service Signs
(White on blue)

1. Telephone
2. Hospital
3. Camping (Tents)
4. Camping (Trailers)
5. Roadside Table

General Information Signs

1. School Crossing Area (*Black on yellow*)
2. Railroad Crossing (*Black on yellow*)
3. No Passing Zone (*Black on yellow*)
4. Bicycle Route (*White on green*)
5. Diagrammatic sign for directional intersection (*White on green*)
6. Bump (*Black on yellow*)

Warning Signs
(Black on yellow)

1. Merge

2. Divided Highway

3. Two-Way Traffic

4. Signal Ahead

5. Hill

6. Slippery When Wet

7. Bicycle Route

8. Pedestrian Crossing

9. Deer Crossing

10. Cattle Crossing

11. Farm Machinery

I *Reading Signs:* Here are some universal signs. What do they mean?

1. _____

2. _____

3. _____

4. _____

5. _____

6. _____

1

2

3

4

5

6

Getting There

What do these signs mean?

1. _____   4. _____

2. _____   5. _____

3. _____

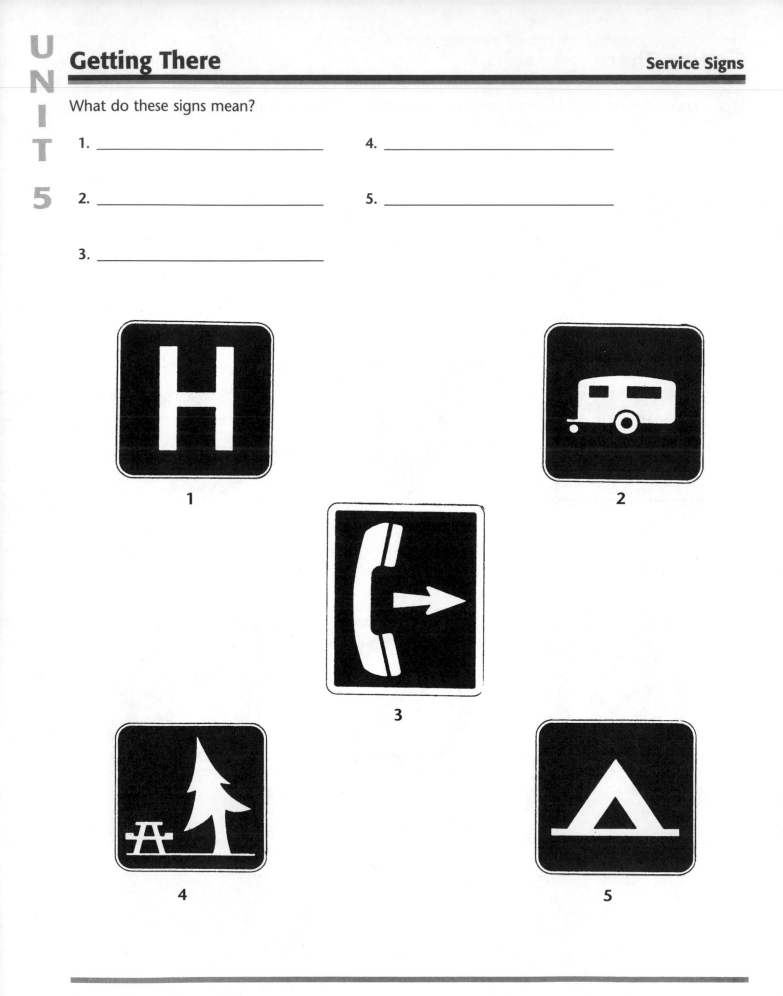

1

2

3

4

5

Getting There

What do these signs mean?

1. _____

2. _____

3. _____

4. _____

5. _____

6. _____

1

2

3

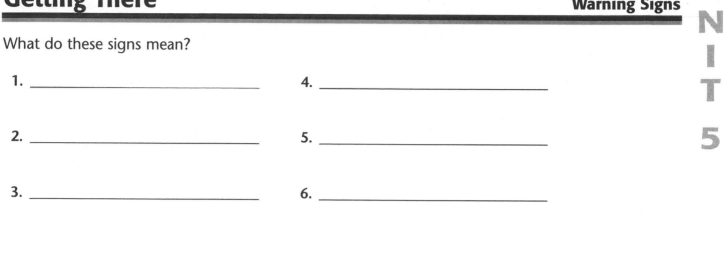

4

5

6

What do these signs mean?

1. _____   4. _____

2. _____   5. _____

3. _____

1

2

3

4

5

What do these signs mean?

1. _____

2. _____

3. _____

4. _____

5. _____

6. _____

1

2

3

4

5

6

J *Plan a Trip:* Following the steps below, plan a vacation for four people. Choose one of these destinations: Orlando, Virginia Beach, or New York City. Pretend that you have $3,000 maximum to cover all expenses for one week's time. This amount must cover **transportation, hotel accommodations, food, entertainment,** and **miscellaneous daily expenses** (taxi fare, tolls, tips, souvenirs are some examples). You'll need a calculator and some separate sheets of paper for this activity. *Hint:* use the yellow pages of a telephone book to get toll-free phone numbers of airlines, hotels, car rental agencies, and ticketing agencies.

1. Choose your destination. _____

2. When will you go? _____

3. How will you travel there? _____ Cost _____

4. Where will you stay when you arrive? _____

   Will you need one or two rooms? _____ *Cost per day* _____

5. What will you do there? *Example:* Day 1 see a musical, Cost: $50/ticket

   Day 1 _____ *Approximate Cost* _____

   Day 2 _____ *Approximate Cost* _____

   Day 3 _____ *Approximate Cost* _____

   Day 4 _____ *Approximate Cost* _____

   Day 5 _____ *Approximate Cost* _____

   Day 6 _____ *Approximate Cost* _____

   Day 7 _____ *Approximate Cost* _____

6. Estimate daily budget for food per person. (Allow for one expensive meal each day.)

   _____

7. How will you pay for things once you get there? *Example*: traveler's checks, credit cards, cash. *Hint:* most resorts and hotels won't accept personal checks.

   _____

8. How will you travel in the city you have selected? *Example:* taxi, walk, rental car.

   Cost per day _____

9. Daily miscellaneous expenses per person _____

10. Make a list of everything you must pack. Since you don't want to be burdened by heavy suitcases, fit everything into one large suitcase and one small one. Clothing (*Hint:* make sure your clothes fit your planned activities.)

_____

_____

Equipment (sunglasses, camera, diving mask/goggles, etc.)

_____

_____

Essentials (money, identification, airline tickets, medicine)

_____

_____

11. Here are some typical problems that occur during vacations. What can you do to prevent or solve them?

Stolen wallet/money_____

Stolen jewelry_____

Sunburn_____

Become lost_____

Run out of your prescription medicine_____

Sore feet_____

Hotel has lost your reservation_____

12. Total your estimated expenses (remember to multiply by 4 for such things as meals, tickets, miscellaneous expenses). Enter the total amount here. Use the form on the next page to help you.

$

If the amount is *more* than $3,000, decide how to lower your expenses.

_____

_____

If the amount is *less* than $3,000—congratulations! You did well!

Estimated Expense Sheet

Trip to _____

1. Travel (round-trip) _____ per person X 4 = _____

2. Lodging _____ per person X 6 days X 4 = _____

3. Daily Activities

   Day 1 _____ per person X 4 = _____

   Day 2 _____ per person X 4 = _____

   Day 3 _____ per person X 4 = _____

   Day 4 _____ per person X 4 = _____

   Day 5 _____ per person X 4 = _____

   Day 6 _____ per person X 4 = _____

   Day 7 _____ per person X 4 = _____

4. Food _____ per person/day X 7 X 4 = _____

5. Miscellaneous _____ per person/day X 7 X 4 = _____
   Travel Expenses

6. Miscellaneous _____ per person/day X 7 X 4 = _____
   Expenses

TOTAL

Transfer total to page 65.

When you begin working and supporting yourself, you may begin planning to move into your own apartment.

When you find a place you like, you may have to fill out a **Rental Application.** The application is a little like an employment application. It asks questions about your background: where you work, how much money you earn. It might even ask for references. Not all landlords will ask you to fill out an application, but all of them will ask you some questions to see if you are responsible.

If the landlord agrees to rent the apartment or house to you, he or she will ask you to sign a **Lease Contract.** It is an agreement between the **lessor** (landlord) and the **lessee** (you). The lease states the amount of rent you have agreed to pay and your responsibilities. It also states the landlord's responsibilities to you. Probably, the lease will also list any rules or regulations of the building.

Before you sign a lease, read it carefully! It is a legal document and you must do everything that you agreed to do—for however long the lease runs. *Remember: there is no such thing as a "standard" lease form, so make sure you understand everything in it.* The lease is often full of legal words; ask the landlord what they mean if you are not sure. Also, fill in all blank spaces on the agreement. This is for your protection.

Here are some important questions to cover in a lease.

➤ What is the length of the lease (one year, six months)?

➤ What amount of rent must you pay and what day of the month is it due?

➤ What repairs or improvements will the landlord make before you move in?

➤ How much is the deposit? What must you do to have it returned?

➤ Are pets allowed? Would you have to pay extra rent or a deposit?

➤ Can you sublet (rent your apartment to someone else during your lease)?

➤ Are utilities (gas, electric, water, garbage pickup) included in the rent? If not, how much did they cost the previous tenant?

➤ Can you (the lessee) paint the apartment? Who pays for the paint?

➤ Does the landlord carry insurance (theft, fire, flood) on the apartment?

➤ Is there a limit to how many people can live in the apartment? Would additional people increase the rent?

➤ Who is responsible for taking care of the outside of the apartment (lawn, sidewalks, alley)?

There are an awful lot of questions to ask, aren't there? Remember that you will spend up to two-thirds of your time in your home, so you will have to live with your decisions for the length of the lease.

A *Using a Rental Application:* Pretend that you are the landlord and fill in all the blanks in the first section of the application. Decide how much rent to charge and what the security deposit will be. When is the rent due? You decide. Then pretend that you are the renter and fill out the remaining information that is needed.

Rental Application

Date _____

Application is hereby made to rent premises known as

_____

Apartment No.   Building Name

_____

Street & Number   City   State   ZIP

for a term of _____ beginning the _____ day

of _____ , 19 _____ , and ending the _____ day of

_____ , 19 _____ , for which monthly rental shall be $_____

payable in advance, and for which a security deposit of $ _____ shall be due prior to occupancy of the above-described premises.

APPLICANT

Name _____

Present Address _____ How Long? _____

Previous Address _____ How Long? _____

Married? _____ Spouse's Name _____ No. to Live in Apt. _____

Children? _____ How Many? _____ Ages? _____

Pets? _____ What Kind? _____ How Many? _____

YOUR EMPLOYMENT

Employer _____

Employer Address _____

Supervisor _____ Bus. Phone _____

How Long on Present Job? _____ Annual Income _____

SPOUSE'S EMPLOYMENT

Employer _____

Employer Address _____

Supervisor _____ Bus. Phone _____

How Long on Present Job? _____ Annual Income _____

REFERENCES

Bank _____ Phone _____

Personal Reference _____ Phone _____

Credit Reference _____ Phone _____

Credit Reference _____ Phone _____

_____
Applicant's Signature

The information provided herein may be used by the landlord or agent to determine whether to accept this application. Upon written request within sixty days, the landlord or agent will disclose to applicant in writing the nature and scope of any investigation landlord has requested and will, if this application is refused, state in writing the reason for said refusal.

Accepted _____ Refused _____ By _____

Your Own Apartment

B *Budgeting for an Apartment:* Pretend your take-home pay is $1,200 per month. You should spend no more than about one-fourth of your take-home pay for rent or *one-third* of your take-home pay for rent and utilities *combined.* Answer questions 1–4, then choose the most economical living situation (question 5) from the three advertisements below.

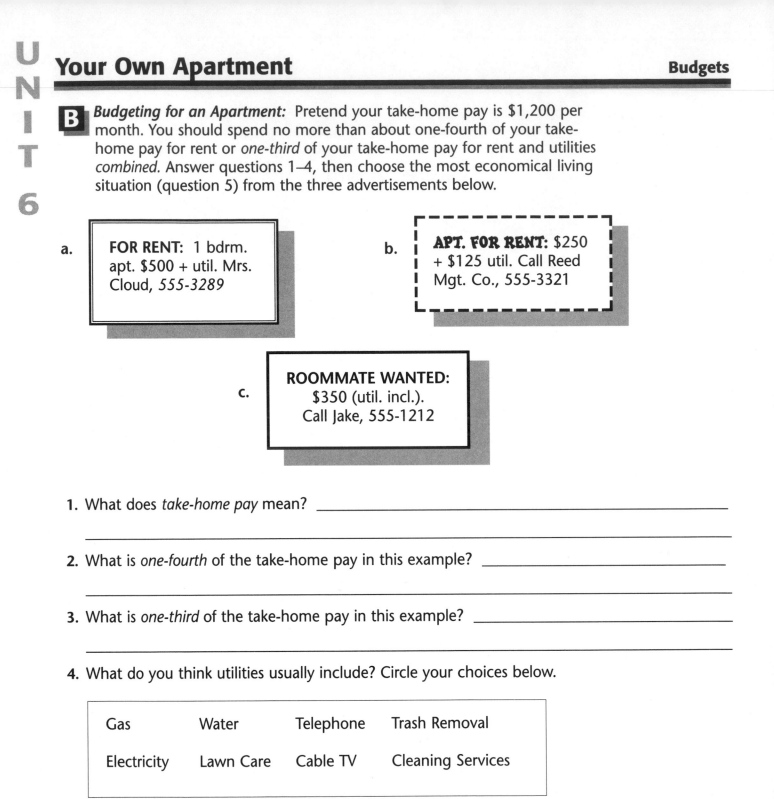

a. **FOR RENT:** 1 bdrm. apt. $500 + util. Mrs. Cloud, *555-3289*

b. **APT. FOR RENT:** $250 + $125 util. Call Reed Mgt. Co., 555-3321

c. **ROOMMATE WANTED:** $350 (util. incl.). Call Jake, 555-1212

1. What does *take-home pay* mean? _____

_____

2. What is *one-fourth* of the take-home pay in this example? _____

_____

3. What is *one-third* of the take-home pay in this example? _____

_____

4. What do you think utilities usually include? Circle your choices below.

Gas	Water	Telephone	Trash Removal
Electricity	Lawn Care	Cable TV	Cleaning Services

5. Based on your answers, choose **a, b,** or **c** as the most economical choice. _____

C *Choosing an Apartment:* Arrange the following steps into the most logical order for leasing an apartment. Place *a, b, c, d,* or *e* next to the numbered steps in the picture above.

a. Sign a lease.

b. Look at several apartments.

c. Give the landlord a deposit.

d. Decide what you can afford.

e. Decide what kind of place you want: do you want to live by yourself or with a roommate? Does the apartment need to be convenient to public transportation? Would an apartment complex be more desirable than a unit in a small building?

D *Find the Word:* Below the box are some of the words people use in leasing an apartment. Find each of these words in the box. Then write a short definition beside each word. The first one is done for you.

B	I	D	R	O	L	D	N	A	L
B	U	I	S	T	N	O	C	E	U
E	O	B	N	T	E	S	S	T	T
E	S	U	P	C	P	S	I	I	E
S	E	D	I	A	O	L	B	S	L
S	D	G	T	R	I	M	A	O	B
E	R	E	N	T	T	E	E	P	U
L	A	T	I	N	L	R	B	E	S
A	D	E	P	O	R	I	T	D	A
E	S	G	U	C	Y	E	N	O	M

1. money   currency _____

2. budget _____

3. lease _____

4. utilities _____

5. deposit _____

6. lessee _____

7. rent _____

8. income _____

9. lessor _____

10. sublet _____

11. landlord _____

12. contract _____

Rights and Responsibilities

One important lesson we must learn as we grow older is that almost everything we want has some kind of price attached to it. We all know that things like cars, clothes, and stereo equipment come with price tags. But *intangible* things— things we cannot touch— have a cost too. For instance, dancing until two o'clock in the morning may be lots of fun, but we will pay for our loss of sleep the next day when we are tired and have no energy.

A safe and secure country, fire and police protection, and unemployment insurance are a few of the intangible privileges we enjoy in this country. In exchange for these benefits, we must handle the responsibilities and duties that come with them. Paying income taxes, voting, doing jury duty, and registering for military service are some of the ways that we pay for the privileges we receive.

Selective Service registration is one of the duties that all adult men must perform in this country. Within thirty days of their eighteenth birthday, all young men must register for the military, usually at the post office or through a postcard received in the mail from the government. This way, the country has a list of possible soldiers in case of national emergency. Currently, American women are not required to register, though this procedure is quite normal in some countries.

Serving on a jury is another important responsibility we as citizens have. To serve on a jury, a person must be a registered voter. Only registered voters are called for jury duty. Registering to vote, voting, and serving on a jury are all ways we participate in the democratic process   so important to helping our country work.

During the remainder of this chapter, you will learn more about your duties, rights, and privileges as an American citizen.

A *Matching Rights and Responsibilities:* Match the right (privilege) in Column 1 with the responsibility in Column 2.

Column 1	Column 2
_____ 1. A voice in government	a. Draft registration
_____ 2. A safe and secure country	b. Jury duty
_____ 3. Trial by jury	c. Voter registration
_____ 4. Safe roadways	d. Taxes
_____ 5. Social programs for the needy	e. Vehicle inspection

Rights and Responsibilities

While registering for the military is an obligation of eighteen-year-olds, **voting** is a right and privilege that arrives at the same age. Your vote equals your voice in our government. Voting means that your opinion is counted as an adult.

You will have the chance to vote for the President of the United States; your state governor and state representatives; representatives to Congress; and your city mayor, sheriff, and council members. You might also vote in a referendum, which is a special issue that affects where you live (like a tax increase).

To vote, you must register with the **Board of Elections.** Its address can be found in the telephone directory.

APPLICATION FOR REGISTRATION
Under penalty of perjury, write the following answers.

1. Your name, the way you want to be registered _____

2. Your date of birth _____

3. Are you a citizen of the United States? _____

4. What is your present home address? _____

If you have not lived at present address for one year, please list previous address where you have lived, going back one year.

_____ from _____ to _____
former address   date moved here   date left

5. Have you ever been convicted of the crime of bribery, theft, arson, obtaining money or goods under false pretense, perjury, forgery, embezzlement, or bigamy? _____

   After you have answered 1 through 5 above, sign the following oath in the presence of the registrar or deputy registrar.

STATE OF
COUNTY OF

_____
APPLICANT SIGN HERE

STATE OF
COUNTY OF

SWORN TO AND SUBSCRIBED BEFORE ME, THE _____ DAY OF _____ , 19_____

H. T. ASHFORD, JR., CIRCUIT CLERK

By _____ D. C.

U N I T 7

Your vote is private. That's why it is called a *secret ballot*. You vote by putting an **X** beside your choice. Sometimes a punch-card system is used, and in other places a special voting machine is used. No matter what system is used, every election has a ballot. The one below is an example.

Official Ballot

To vote a straight party ticket, mark a cross (X) or check mark (✓) in the square, in the Party Column opposite the name of the party of your choice. A cross (X) or check mark (✓) in the square opposite the name of any candidate indicates a vote for that candidate. To vote for a person whose name is not on the ballot, write, print, or paste his or her name in the blank space provided for that purpose. This shall count as a vote without the cross (X) or check mark (✓). To vote for an individual candidate of another party after making a mark in the party square, mark a cross (X) or check mark (✓) opposite his or her name. For an office where more than one candidate is to be elected, the voter, after marking in the party square, may divide his or her vote by marking a cross (X) or check mark (✓) to the right of each candidate for whom he or she desires to vote. For such offices, votes shall not be counted for candidates not individually marked. If you make a mistake, do not erase. Ask for a new ballot. Use only black lead pencil, indelible pencil, or blue, black, or blue-black ink in fountain pen or ballpoint pen. Use the same pencil for all markings you place on the ballot.

PARTY COLUMN

TO VOTE A STRAIGHT PARTY TICKET MARK A CROSS (X) OR CHECK MARK (✓) IN THIS COLUMN.

DEMOCRATIC	
REPUBLICAN	
CONSTITUTIONAL	
LIBERTY	

JUSTICE OF THE SUPREME COURT
(Vote for Two)

Lana L. Mandarin	Democratic	☐
Radcliff C. N. Near	Republican	☐
Grace Eppley	Constitutional	☐
Andrea F. Barzutti	Liberty	☐

DISTRICT ATTORNEY (Vote for One)

Culber J. Abraham	Democratic	☐
Laban L. Corothy	Republican	☐

REGISTRAR OF WILLS (Vote for One)

Will D. Shantz	Democratic	☐
T. T. (Terence) Medlinger	Republican	☐

RECORDER OF DEEDS (Vote for One)

Richmond E. Carey, Jr.	Democratic	☐
Eldridge B. Jones	Republican	☐

COUNTY TREASURER (Vote for One)

T. Ethan Marr	Democratic	☐
Seymour G. Gillis	Republican	☐

CLERK OF THE COURTS (Vote for One)

Shane D. O'Brien	Democratic	☐
Jabey (Aubin) Hildebrande	Republican	☐

CORONER (Vote for One)

Jeremiah J. Gascha	Democratic	☐
Jarvis A. Marvin	Republican	☐

SUPERVISOR (Vote for One)

Fulton J. Antozzio	Democratic	☐
Hubert R. Busch	Republican	☐

SCHOOL DIRECTOR (Vote for One)
(Attendale Area School District)

Lee A. Grabewski	Democratic	☐

By April 15 of each year you must pay **Federal Income Tax.** This can be a complicated process. Volumes of books have been written about filing your income tax return.

Before income tax time, you will receive a **Wage and Tax Statement (W–2 Form).** This form shows how much money you earned and how much money was deducted for taxes. Sometimes, too much money is taken out by your employer and the government owes you a **refund.** If not enough was taken out, you then owe the government the balance. You should get a separate W-2 form from each employer you may have in a year.

The following is an example of a Wage and Tax Statement:

a Control number	22222	Void ☐	For Official Use Only ▶ OMB No. 1545-0008		
b Employer's identification number 10-000-2			1 Wages, tips, and other compensation 15155.34		2 Federal income tax withheld 1756.00
c Employer's name. address. and ZIP code United Lumber Co. 901 Timber Lane Woodville, WA 48486			3 Social security wages 15155.34		4 Social security tax withheld 1083.60
			5 Medicare wages and tips		6 Medicare tax withheld
			7 Social security tips		8 Allocated tips
d Employee's social security number 234-56-7890			9 Advance EIC payment		10 Dependent care benefits
e Employee's name (first, middle initial, last) David B. Swanson 4232 Plantation Avenue Salem, OR 97301			11 Nonqualified plans		12 Benefits included in box 1
			13 See Instrs. for box 13		14 Other
f Employee's address and ZIP code			15 Statutory employee ☐ Deceased ☐ Pension plan ☐ Legal rep. ☐ Hshld. emp. ☐ Subtotal ☐ Deferred compensation ☐		

16 State Employer's state I.D. No. OR 98-768-0	17 State wages. tips. etc. 15155.34	18 State income tax 564.35	19 Locality name	20 Local wages. tips. etc.	21 Local income tax

Cat. No. 10134D

Department of the Treasury—Internal Revenue Service

Form **W-2** **Wage and Tax Statement** **1996**

For Paperwork Reduction Act Notice, see separate instructions.

Copy A For Social Security Administration

Notice that the W-2 Form shows how much money was deducted for federal income taxes, state taxes, and Social Security tax. Sometimes city or local taxes are also withheld. Before beginning to fill out your tax forms, gather all the materials and information you will need.

B ***Getting Ready to Do Your Taxes:*** Look over the 1040 income tax forms that follow. Then put an X in front of the materials or information a person would need to have handy before filling in the income tax forms.

_____ 1. calculator

_____ 2. doctor's name

_____ 3. bank interest statements

_____ 4. credit card numbers

_____ 5. insurance card

_____ 6. apartment lease

_____ 7. tax instruction book

_____ 8. pens and pencils

_____ 9. child care costs

_____ 10. receipts for charitable contributions

_____ 11. medical receipts

_____ 12. W-2 Form

_____ 13. Social Security number

_____ 14. checkbook

_____ 15. newspaper

_____ 16. IRA deposit statements

_____ 17. stamps

_____ 18. car license

_____ 19. mortgage interest statement

_____ 20. Social Security numbers of children

This is a sample of Form 1040 that is used for filing your Income Tax.

Form **1040**	Department of the Treasury—Internal Revenue Service **U.S. Individual Income Tax Return**	**1995**	(10)	IRS Use Only—Do not write or staple in this space.

For the year Jan. 1–Dec. 31, 1995, or other tax year beginning _____ , 1995, ending _____ , 19 ___ | OMB No. 1545-0074

Label
(See instructions on page 11.)

Use the IRS label. Otherwise, please print or type.

Your first name and initial	Last name	Your social security number
David B.	Swanson	234 56 7890
If a joint return, spouse's first name and initial	Last name	Spouse's social security number

Home address (number and street). If you have a P.O. box, see page 11. | Apt. no.
4232 Plantation Ave.

For Privacy Act and Paperwork Reduction Act Notice, see page 7.

City, town or post office, state, and ZIP code. If you have a foreign address, see page 11.
Salem, OR 97301

Presidential Election Campaign
(See page 11.)
▶ Do you want $3 to go to this fund? . . . .
If a joint return, does your spouse want $3 to go to this fund? . . . .

	Yes	No	Note: Checking "Yes" will not change your tax or reduce your refund.
		✓	

Filing Status
(See page 11.)

Check only one box.

1 ✓ Single
2 ☐ Married filing joint return (even if only one had income)
3 ☐ Married filing separate return. Enter spouse's social security no. above and full name here. ▶ _____
4 ☐ Head of household (with qualifying person). (See page 12.) If the qualifying person is a child but not your dependent, enter this child's name here. ▶ _____
5 ☐ Qualifying widow(er) with dependent child (year spouse died ▶ 19 ___). (See page 12.)

Exemptions
(See page 12.)

If more than six dependents, see page 13.

6a ✓ **Yourself.** If your parent (or someone else) can claim you as a dependent on his or her tax return, **do not** check box 6a. But be sure to check the box on line 33b on page 2
b ☐ **Spouse** . . . .
c **Dependents:**

(1) First name Last name	(2) Dependent's social security number. If born in 1995, see page 13.	(3) Dependent's relationship to you	(4) No. of months lived in your home in 1995

d If your child didn't live with you but is claimed as your dependent under a pre-1985 agreement, check here ▶ ☐
e Total number of exemptions claimed . . . .

No. of boxes checked on 6a and 6b: **1**
No. of your children on 6c who:
• lived with you ___
• didn't live with you due to divorce or separation (see page 14) ___
Dependents on 6c not entered above ___
Add numbers entered on lines above ▶ **1**

Income

Attach Copy B of your Forms W-2, W-2G, and 1099-R here.

If you did not get a W-2, see page 14.

Enclose, but do not attach, your payment and payment voucher. See page 33.

7	Wages, salaries, tips, etc. Attach Form(s) W-2	7	$15,155 34
8a	Taxable Interest income (see page 15). Attach Schedule B if over $400	8a	
b	Tax-exempt interest (see page 15). DON'T include on line 8a	8b	
9	Dividend income. Attach Schedule B if over $400	9	
10	Taxable refunds, credits, or offsets of state and local income taxes (see page 15) . .	10	
11	Alimony received	11	
12	Business income or (loss). Attach Schedule C or C-EZ	12	
13	Capital gain or (loss). If required, attach Schedule D (see page 16) . . .	13	
14	Other gains or (losses). Attach Form 4797	14	
15a	Total IRA distributions . 15a ___ b Taxable amount (see page 16)	15b	
16a	Total pensions and annuities 16a ___ b Taxable amount (see page 16)	16b	
17	Rental real estate, royalties, partnerships, S corporations, trusts, etc. Attach Schedule E	17	
18	Farm income or (loss). Attach Schedule F	18	
19	Unemployment compensation (see page 17)	19	
20a	Social security benefits 20a ___ b Taxable amount (see page 18)	20b	
21	Other income. List type and amount—see page 18 _____	21	
22	Add the amounts in the far right column for lines 7 through 21. This is your **total income** ▶	22	15,155 34

Adjustments to Income

23a	Your IRA deduction (see page 19)	23a	
b	Spouse's IRA deduction (see page 19)	23b	
24	Moving expenses. Attach Form 3903 or 3903-F . . .	24	
25	One-half of self-employment tax	25	
26	Self-employed health insurance deduction (see page 21)	26	
27	Keogh & self-employed SEP plans. If SEP, check ▶ ☐	27	
28	Penalty on early withdrawal of savings	28	
29	Alimony paid. Recipient's SSN ▶ ___ ___ ___	29	
30	Add lines 23a through 29. These are your **total adjustments** . . . . ▶	30	

Adjusted Gross Income

31	Subtract line 30 from line 22. This is your **adjusted gross income.** If less than $26,673 and a child lived with you (less than $9,230 if a child didn't live with you), see "Earned Income Credit" on page 27 ▶	31	15,155 34

Cat. No. 11320B   Form **1040** (1995)

Form 1040 (1995)   Page **2**

Tax Computation

(See page 23.)

32	Amount from line 31 (adjusted gross income)	**32** 15,155 34

33a Check if: ☐ **You** were 65 or older, ☐ Blind; ☐ **Spouse** was 65 or older, ☐ Blind.
Add the number of boxes checked above and enter the total here . . . . ▶ **33a** ☐

b If your parent (or someone else) can claim you as a dependent, check here . ▶ **33b** ☐

c If you are married filing separately and your spouse itemizes deductions or you are a dual-status alien, see page 23 and check here . . . . ▶ **33c** ☐

34 Enter the larger of your: { **Itemized deductions** from Schedule A, line 28, **OR**
Standard deduction shown below for your filing status. **But if you checked any box on line 33a or b,** go to page 23 to find your standard deduction. If you checked **box 33c,** your standard deduction is zero.
● Single—$3,900   ● Married filing jointly or Qualifying widow(er)—$6,550
● Head of household—$5,750   ● Married filing separately—$3,275 }   **34** 3,900 00

35 Subtract line 34 from line 32 . . . .   **35** 11,255 34

36 If line 32 is $86,025 or less, multiply $2,500 by the total number of exemptions claimed on line 6e. If line 32 is over $86,025, see the worksheet on page 23 for the amount to enter .   **36** 2,500 00

If you want the IRS to figure your tax, see page 35.

37 **Taxable income.** Subtract line 36 from line 35. If line 36 is more than line 35, enter -0-   **37** 8,755 34

38 Tax. Check if from a ☑ Tax Table, b ☐ Tax Rate Schedules, c ☐ Capital Gain Tax Worksheet, or d ☐ Form 8615 (see page 24). Amount from Form(s) 8814 ▶ e _____| **38** 1,316 00

39 Additional taxes. Check if from a ☐ Form 4970 b ☐ Form 4972 . . . .   **39**

40 Add lines 38 and 39 . . . . ▶   **40** 1,316 00

Credits

(See page 24.)

		41	
41	Credit for child and dependent care expenses. Attach Form 2441		
42	Credit for the elderly or the disabled. Attach Schedule R . .	42	
43	Foreign tax credit. Attach Form 1116	43	
44	Other credits (see page 25). Check if from a ☐ Form 3800 b ☐ Form 8396 c ☐ Form 8801 d ☐ Form (specify) ____	44	

45 Add lines 41 through 44 . . . .   **45**

46 Subtract line 45 from line 40. If line 45 is more than line 40, enter -0- . . . . ▶   **46** 1,316 00

Other Taxes

(See page 25.)

47 Self-employment tax. Attach Schedule SE **47**

48 Alternative minimum tax. Attach Form 6251 . . . .   **48**

49 Recapture taxes. Check if from a ☐ Form 4255 b ☐ Form 8611 c ☐ Form 8828   **49**

50 Social security and Medicare tax on tip income not reported to employer. Attach Form 4137   **50**

51 Tax on qualified retirement plans, including IRAs. If required, attach Form 5329 . . . .   **51**

52 Advance earned income credit payments from Form W-2 . . . .   **52**

53 Household employment taxes. Attach Schedule H **53**

54 Add lines 46 through 53. This is your **total tax** . . . . ▶   **54** 1,316 00

Payments

Attach Forms W-2, W-2G, and 1099-R on the front.

55	Federal income tax withheld. If any is from Form(s) 1099, check ▶ ☐	55	1,756 00
56	1995 estimated tax payments and amount applied from 1994 return .	56	
57	**Earned income credit.** Attach Schedule EIC if you have a qualifying child. Nontaxable earned income: amount ▶ [___|___] and type ▶	57	
58	Amount paid with Form 4868 (extension request)	58	
59	Excess social security and RRTA tax withheld (see page 32) .	59	
60	Other payments. Check if from a ☐ Form 2439 b ☐ Form 4136	60	

61 Add lines 55 through 60. These are your **total payments** . . . . ▶   **61** 1,756 00

Refund or Amount You Owe

62 If line 61 is more than line 54, subtract line 54 from line 61. This is the amount you **OVERPAID** . . .   **62** 440 00

63 Amount of line 62 you want **REFUNDED TO YOU.** . . . . ▶   **63** 440 00

64 Amount of line 62 you want **APPLIED TO YOUR 1996 ESTIMATED TAX** ▶ [**64** |]

65 If line 54 is more than line 61, subtract line 61 from line 54. This is the **AMOUNT YOU OWE.** For details on how to pay and use **Form 1040-V,** Payment Voucher, see page 33 . . ▶   **65**

66 Estimated tax penalty (see page 33). Also include on line 65 [**66** |]

Sign Here

Keep a copy of this return for your records.

Under penalties of perjury, I declare that I have examined this return and accompanying schedules and statements, and to the best of my knowledge and belief, they are true, correct, and complete. Declaration of preparer (other than taxpayer) is based on all information of which preparer has any knowledge.

Your signature	Date	Your occupation
David B. Swanson	4/14/96	Lumberjack
Spouse's signature. If a joint return, BOTH must sign.	Date	Spouse's occupation

Paid Preparer's Use Only

Preparer's signature ▶	Date	Check if self-employed ☐	Preparer's social security no.
Firm's name (or yours if self-employed) and address ▶		EIN	
		ZIP code	

C *Completing an Income Tax Form:* Try filling out an income tax form. Invent the requested information, like income, taxes withheld, and amount owed (or due to be refunded). Pretend you are single and have no children.

Form **1040**	Department of the Treasury—Internal Revenue Service **U.S. Individual Income Tax Return** **1995**	(10)	IRS Use Only—Do not write or staple in this space.

For the year Jan. 1–Dec. 31, 1995, or other tax year beginning _____ , 1995, ending _____ , 19 ___ | OMB No. 1545-0074

Label

(See instructions on page 11.)

Use the IRS label. Otherwise, please print or type.

L A B E L   H E R E

Your first name and initial _____ Last name _____

Your social security number _____

If a joint return, spouse's first name and initial _____ Last name _____

Spouse's social security number _____

Home address (number and street). If you have a P.O. box, see page 11. _____ Apt. no. ____

City, town or post office, state, and ZIP code. If you have a foreign address, see page 11. _____

For Privacy Act and Paperwork Reduction Act Notice, see page 7.

Presidential Election Campaign (See page 11.) ▶

Do you want $3 to go to this fund? . . . . Yes [ ] No [ ]

If a joint return, does your spouse want $3 to go to this fund? . . . . Yes [ ] No [ ]

Note: *Checking "Yes" will not change your tax or reduce your refund.*

Filing Status

(See page 11.)

Check only one box.

1 [ ] Single

2 [ ] Married filing joint return (even if only one had income)

3 [ ] Married filing separate return. Enter spouse's social security no. above and full name here. ▶ _____

4 [ ] Head of household (with qualifying person). (See page 12.) If the qualifying person is a child but not your dependent, enter this child's name here. ▶ _____

5 [ ] Qualifying widow(er) with dependent child (year spouse died ▶ 19 ___). (See page 12.)

Exemptions

(See page 12.)

If more than six dependents, see page 13.

6a [ ] **Yourself.** If your parent (or someone else) can claim you as a dependent on his or her tax return, **do not** check box 6a. But be sure to check the box on line 33b on page 2 . }

b [ ] **Spouse** . . . . }

No. of boxes checked on 6a and 6b ____

c **Dependents:**

(1) First name Last name	(2) Dependent's social security number. If born in 1995, see page 13.	(3) Dependent's relationship to you	(4) No. of months lived in your home in 1995
_____	_____	_____	_____
_____	_____	_____	_____
_____	_____	_____	_____
_____	_____	_____	_____

No. of your children on 6c who:
- **lived with you** ____
- **didn't live with you due to divorce or separation (see page 14)** ____

Dependents on 6c not entered above ____

d If your child didn't live with you but is claimed as your dependent under a pre-1985 agreement, check here ▶ [ ]

e Total number of exemptions claimed . . . .

Add numbers entered on lines above ▶ [ ]

Income

Attach Copy B of your Forms W-2, W-2G, and 1099-R here.

If you did not get a W-2, see page 14.

Enclose, but do not attach, your payment and payment voucher. See page 33.

7 Wages, salaries, tips, etc. Attach Form(s) W-2 . . . . | **7** |

8a **Taxable** interest income (see page 15). Attach Schedule B if over $400 . . . . | **8a** |

b **Tax-exempt** interest (see page 15). DON'T include on line 8a | **8b** |

9 Dividend income. Attach Schedule B if over $400 . . . . | **9** |

10 Taxable refunds, credits, or offsets of state and local income taxes (see page 15) . . | **10** |

11 Alimony received . . . . | **11** |

12 Business income or (loss). Attach Schedule C or C-EZ . . . . . . | **12** |

13 Capital gain or (loss). If required, attach Schedule D (see page 16) . . | **13** |

14 Other gains or (losses). Attach Form 4797 . . . . | **14** |

15a Total IRA distributions . | 15a | b Taxable amount (see page 16) | **15b** |

16a Total pensions and annuities | 16a | b Taxable amount (see page 16) | **16b** |

17 Rental real estate, royalties, partnerships, S corporations, trusts, etc. Attach Schedule E | **17** |

18 Farm income or (loss). Attach Schedule F . . . . | **18** |

19 Unemployment compensation (see page 17) . . . . | **19** |

20a Social security benefits | 20a | b Taxable amount (see page 18) | **20b** |

21 Other income. List type and amount—see page 18 _____ | **21** |

22 Add the amounts in the far right column for lines 7 through 21. This is your **total income** ▶ | **22** |

Adjustments to Income

23a Your IRA deduction (see page 19) . . . . | 23a |

b Spouse's IRA deduction (see page 19) . . . . . | 23b |

24 Moving expenses. Attach Form 3903 or 3903-F . . . | 24 |

25 One-half of self-employment tax . . . . | 25 |

26 Self-employed health insurance deduction (see page 21) | 26 |

27 Keogh & self-employed SEP plans. If SEP, check ▶ [ ] | 27 |

28 Penalty on early withdrawal of savings . . . . . | 28 |

29 Alimony paid. Recipient's SSN ▶ _____ | 29 |

30 Add lines 23a through 29. These are your **total adjustments** . . . . ▶ | **30** |

Adjusted Gross Income

31 Subtract line 30 from line 22. This is your **adjusted gross income.** If less than $26,673 and a child lived with you (less than $9,230 if a child didn't live with you), see "Earned Income Credit" on page 27 ▶ | **31** |

Cat. No. 11320B

Form **1040** (1995)

Form 1040 (1995)   Page **2**

Tax Compu- tation (See page 23.)	**32**	Amount from line 31 (adjusted gross income)	**32**	
	33a	Check if: ☐ **You** were 65 or older, ☐ Blind; ☐ **Spouse** was 65 or older, ☐ Blind. Add the number of boxes checked above and enter the total here . . . . ▶ **33a**		
	b	If your parent (or someone else) can claim you as a dependent, check here . ▶ **33b** ☐		
	c	If you are married filing separately and your spouse itemizes deductions or you are a dual-status alien, see page 23 and check here . . . . ▶ **33c** ☐		
	34	Enter the **larger** of your: { **Itemized deductions** from Schedule A, line 28, **OR** **Standard deduction** shown below for your filing status. **But if you checked any box on line 33a or b,** go to page 23 to find your standard deduction. If you checked **box 33c,** your standard deduction is zero. ● Single—$3,900 ● Married filing jointly or Qualifying widow(er)—$6,550 ● Head of household—$5,750 ● Married filing separately—$3,275 }	**34**	
	35	Subtract line 34 from line 32	**35**	
If you want the IRS to figure your tax, see page 35.	**36**	If line 32 is $86,025 or less, multiply $2,500 by the total number of exemptions claimed on line 6e. If line 32 is over $86,025, see the worksheet on page 23 for the amount to enter .	**36**	
	37	**Taxable income.** Subtract line 36 from line 35. If line 36 is more than line 35, enter -0- .	**37**	
	38	Tax. Check if from a ☐ Tax Table, b ☐ Tax Rate Schedules, c ☐ Capital Gain Tax Work-sheet, or d ☐ Form 8615 (see page 24). Amount from Form(s) 8814 ▶ e _____	**38**	
	39	Additional taxes. Check if from a ☐ Form 4970 b ☐ Form 4972	**39**	
	40	Add lines 38 and 39 . . . . ▶	**40**	

Credits (See page 24.)	**41**	Credit for child and dependent care expenses. Attach Form 2441	**41**		
	42	Credit for the elderly or the disabled. Attach Schedule R .	**42**		
	43	Foreign tax credit. Attach Form 1116	**43**		
	44	Other credits (see page 25). Check if from a ☐ Form 3800 b ☐ Form 8396 c ☐ Form 8801 d ☐ Form (specify) ____	**44**		
	45	Add lines 41 through 44		**45**	
	46	Subtract line 45 from line 40. If line 45 is more than line 40, enter -0- . . . . . ▶		**46**	

Other Taxes (See page 25.)	**47**	Self-employment tax. Attach Schedule SE	**47**	
	48	Alternative minimum tax. Attach Form 6251	**48**	
	49	Recapture taxes. Check if from a ☐ Form 4255 b ☐ Form 8611 c ☐ Form 8828	**49**	
	50	Social security and Medicare tax on tip income not reported to employer. Attach Form 4137	**50**	
	51	Tax on qualified retirement plans, including IRAs. If required, attach Form 5329 . . .	**51**	
	52	Advance earned income credit payments from Form W-2	**52**	
	53	Household employment taxes. Attach Schedule H	**53**	
	54	Add lines 46 through 53. This is your **total tax** . . . . ▶	**54**	

Payments Attach Forms W-2, W-2G, and 1099-R on the front.	**55**	Federal income tax withheld. If any is from Form(s) 1099, check ▶ ☐	**55**		
	56	1995 estimated tax payments and amount applied from 1994 return .	**56**		
	57	**Earned income credit.** Attach Schedule EIC if you have a qualifying child. Nontaxable earned income: amount ▶ [_____] and type ▶ -------------------	**57**		
	58	Amount paid with Form 4868 (extension request)	**58**		
	59	Excess social security and RRTA tax withheld (see page 32) .	**59**		
	60	Other payments. Check if from a ☐ Form 2439 b ☐ Form 4136	**60**		
	61	Add lines 55 through 60. These are your **total payments** . . . . ▶		**61**	

Refund or Amount You Owe	**62**	If line 61 is more than line 54, subtract line 54 from line 61. This is the amount you **OVERPAID** . .	**62**	
	63	Amount of line 62 you want **REFUNDED TO YOU**. . . . . ▶	**63**	
	64	Amount of line 62 you want **APPLIED TO YOUR 1996 ESTIMATED TAX** ▶ **64**		
	65	If line 54 is more than line 61, subtract line 61 from line 54. This is the **AMOUNT YOU OWE**. For details on how to pay and use **Form 1040-V,** Payment Voucher, see page 33 . . ▶	**65**	
	66	Estimated tax penalty (see page 33). Also include on line 65	**66**		

Sign Here Keep a copy of this return for your records.	Under penalties of perjury, I declare that I have examined this return and accompanying schedules and statements, and to the best of my knowledge and belief, they are true, correct, and complete. Declaration of preparer (other than taxpayer) is based on all information of which preparer has any knowledge. Your signature ___ Date ___ Your occupation ___ Spouse's signature. If a joint return, BOTH must sign. ___ Date ___ Spouse's occupation ___
Paid Preparer's Use Only	Preparer's signature ▶ ___ Date ___ Check if self-employed ☐ Preparer's social security no. ___ Firm's name (or yours if self-employed) and address ▶ ___ EIN ___ ZIP code ___

Rights and Responsibilities

D *Identifying Social Services:* Match each government agency in Column 1 with its description in Column 2. Write the correct letter in the space provided.

Column 1	Column 2
_____ 1. Welfare Assistance	a. Places qualified families into affordable homes or apartments
_____ 2. Employment and Training	b. Provides income assistance to people earning below the national average
_____ 3. Selective Service	c. Provides information and advice to people interested in starting their own business or who own a small business
_____ 4. Housing Authority	d. Provides income assistance to the elderly (65 and older), disabled people who cannot work, and widows and orphans
_____ 5. Internal Revenue Service	e. Registers and authorizes people to vote
_____ 6. Voters' Registration	f. Processes and collects people's annual income tax
_____ 7. Social Security	g. Offers information and services to people who have served in the U.S. military
_____ 8. Department of Motor Vehicles	h. Helps qualified people find jobs and training; provides temporary income assistance during the job search
_____ 9. Small Business Administration	i. Issues driver's permits, licenses, and vehicle registration certificates; conducts driving tests
_____ 10. Veterans Administration	j. Maintains a list of eligible young men to serve in the military in case of war or national emergency

As a citizen of this country, you have the right to apply for help if you need food, a job, or a place to live. As a taxpayer, you help pay for these benefits and programs that are operated by the government. On the next few pages, you will find an application for housing assistance and an application for food stamps. Food stamps can be used in place of money at grocery stores and other places that sell packaged food.

Notice how much information these forms request. You must answer these questions to find out if you *qualify* (meet the requirements) for government assistance.

E *Using Assistance Forms:* Practice filling out these applications for assistance. Make sure you answer every question. Invent answers if necessary for this activity, but don't make up information on the real thing! Inaccurate information can prevent you from receiving help.

APPLICATION FOR HOME IN
HOUSING AUTHORITY DEVELOPMENTS

(PLEASE PRINT)
NAME _____

      (Last)   (Husband's First Name)   (Wife's First Name)   (Wife's Maiden Name)

PRESENT HOME ADDRESS_____ ZIP CODE _____

ADDRESS FOR
PAST 12 MONTHS _____ FROM _____TO _____

                      _____ FROM _____TO _____

HOW LONG HAVE YOU LIVED IN JOHNSTOWN? _____ TELEPHONE _____

IF HUSBAND OR WIFE WILL NOT LIVE WITH FAMILY, STATE REASON _____

ARE YOU A CITIZEN OF THE UNITED STATES? _____

LIST THOSE WHO WILL LIVE TOGETHER IN THE UNIT	SEX	BIRTH DATE			RELATION TO HEAD	EMPLOYED	
		MONTH	DAY	YEAR		YES	NO
1.							
2.							
3.							
4.							
5.							

NAME OF NEAREST RELATIVE _____
(TO CONTACT IN CASE OF EMERGENCY)
ADDRESS _____

CHECK SOURCE OF INCOME OTHER THAN EMPLOYMENT: (Submit Proof)

UNEMPLOYMENT COMPENSATION: AMOUNT $ _____ SOURCE _____

MILITARY SERVICE ALLOTMENT: AMOUNT $ _____ FROM WHOM _____

DEPARTMENT OF PUBLIC ASSISTANCE: AMOUNT $ _____

CONTRIBUTIONS FROM RELATIVES: AMOUNT $ _____

COURT ORDER: AMOUNT $ _____ FOR WHOM _____

                          FROM _____

VETERAN'S PENSION: AMOUNT $ _____ FILE OR CLAIM NO. _____

VETERAN'S EDUCATION SUBSISTENCE ALLOWANCE: AMOUNT $ _____

SOCIAL SECURITY BENEFITS: AMOUNT $ _____ RECEIVED BY _____

INSURANCE BENEFITS: AMOUNT $ _____ RECEIVED BY: _____

OTHER _____ AMOUNT $ _____ SOURCE _____

BANK OR PROPERTY ASSETS: AMOUNT $ _____ SOURCE _____

PRESENT HOUSING SITUATION–(Check the number that applies to your situation)

_____ 1. FORCED TO MOVE (Attach Landlord's Notice To Move)

_____ 2. LIVING DOUBLED UP

_____ 3. FAMILY SEPARATED

_____ 4. SUBSTANDARD HOUSING

_____ 5. NO HOUSING EXPLAIN: _____

_____ 6. ACCOMMODATIONS UNSATISFACTORY BECAUSE OF UNUSUAL CONDITIONS AFFECTING FAMILY

LANDLORD _____ ADDRESS _____

DESCRIBE THE CONDITIONS CHECKED _____

PRESENT RENT _____ UTILITIES _____ TOTAL _____

I do hereby solemnly swear and affirm that the above information is complete and true to the best of my knowledge and belief. I have no objections to inquiries for the purpose of verifying the above information.

               SIGNED _____

                       (Applicant)

DEPARTMENT OF EMPLOYMENT & SOCIAL SERVICES
Social Services Administration
APPLICATION FOR PARTICIPATION IN FOOD STAMP PROGRAM

INSTRUCTIONS FOR COMPLETING THIS FORM: Complete all items. For items not applicable to you, write, "N/A," unless instructions indicate otherwise. Complete form with a typewriter, or print neatly.

1. Name of Head of Household: Last, First, Middle	2. CASE NUMBER: (Worker Completion) FS– PA–	3. DATE:

4. TELEPHONE NUMBERS: (Home & Business)	5. SOURCE OF INFORMATION: ❑ Office Visit ❑ Telephone ❑ Other

6. WITHHOLDING INFORMATION: If you receive public assistance payments, do you wish to have the total cost of your food stamps withheld from your monthly check?   ❑ Yes   ❑ No

7. YOUR RESIDENCE ADDRESS:

(Street or Route Numbers)   (City)   (County)   (State)   (ZIP)

8. DIRECTIONS TO HOME: (Worker Completion Only)

9. YOUR MAILING ADDRESS (If different from residence address):

(Street or Route Numbers)   (City)   (County)   (State)   (ZIP)

10. GIVE THE FOLLOWING INFORMATION FOR ALL PERSONS LIVING IN YOUR HOUSEHOLD EXCEPT ROOMS, BOARDERS, OR PERSONS WHO PROVIDE NURSING CARE, HOUSEKEEPING SERVICE, OR CHILD CARE. LIST THESE EXCEPTIONS IN SECTION 10a BELOW. (List any additional members on a separate sheet and attach.)

Name (Last, First, Middle)	Social Security No.	Date of Birth	Age	Relationship to Head of Household (son, wife, mother-in-law, etc.) If unrelated, enter "None"	Citizen or Alien Status (See Notes 1, 2, 3, & 4 below)	Employment Status (See Notes A, B, C, D, E, F, G, and H)	Work Registration Form (FNS-284) for each member marked "H" Yes No
				HEAD OF HOUSEHOLD			

CITIZEN & ALIEN STATUS	EMPLOYMENT STATUS CODES	
1. U. S. Citizen	A. Household member with responsibility for care of sick, disabled, or dependent children under 18.	E. Persons self-employed on a full-time basis.
2. Permanent Resident alien	B. Students enrolled in a school or training program.	F. Under 18 years of age.
3. Temporary Resident alien	C. Persons working at least 30 hours per week.	G. Over 65 years of age.
4. None of the above	D. Persons unable to work for mental or physical reasons. (Attach doctor's certificate confirming same)	H. Available for employment (Such persons must complete Form FNS-284, Work Registration, before eligibility for Food Stamps can be established)

10a. List persons living in your home who are NOT INCLUDED in Section 10 above. If there are no such persons, write "NONE."

NAME	REASON NOT INCLUDED

Thinking Ahead

Throughout this workbook, you have practiced using many of the forms that you must understand as an adult. Knowing about them will make you more *confident* later on. Confidence is one of the traits that most successful people share. Having **goals** is another trait. In this last chapter, you will learn how goal setting may help you become more successful.

Think about some of the things you want right now. Do you want independence, more money, popularity, or a home of your own? Do you want to learn to play the piano, improve your bowling game, or get along better with your family and friends? Any or all of these things are valuable goals. But how do you achieve them?

Successful people will tell you that they *plan extensively* to obtain the things they want. Most business owners charted how they would own and operate their business, step by step. Olympic athletes arrive at their victories the same way: they decide exactly what they want and then plan how to get it. A businessperson, for example, may decide to open a pizza delivery service that specializes in fast delivery. Then, as the business goes well, the owner may decide to expand the kinds of pizzas sold or the area in which to sell them. In the same way, a swimmer may begin with ten laps per day and increase to twenty laps the following month and thirty laps the third month. Soon, the swimmer's speed and strength have increased to competitive levels.

It is often said that "even the longest journey must begin with the first step." However, no one says how large a step it must be! You can decide to make this last chapter *your* first step in getting some of the things you want most.

In the remainder of this chapter, you will learn some basics in reaching your goals. Take a moment right now and think about some of the things you want. Imagine yourself as being/having/doing whatever relates to your goals. Then write down two of these goals below.

1. _____

2. _____

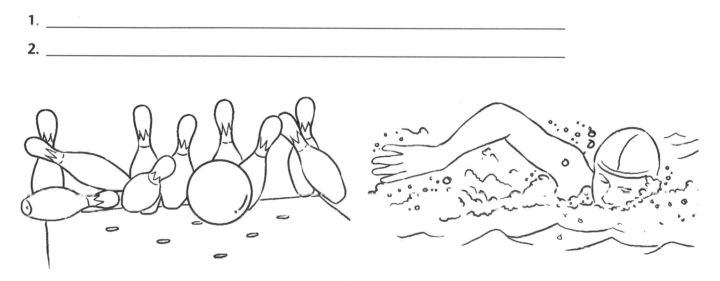

Thinking Ahead

Setting Goals: One common characteristic of successful people is that they set goals for themselves throughout their lives. Having a vague idea about what you want—like wanting to be successful or wealthy—does not usually get you those things. Goals must be very **specific** and **measurable** and include a **time frame.** They also should include a variety of your interests and values. While goals should be all these things, you should remember that goals can and should be changed periodically to reflect the changes in your wants and needs.

Below is an example of how a person might chart his or her goals. Notice the italicized words. They are specific, include a time frame, and are measurable.

Career	• become an *accountant* for a *large corporation* • earn *$25,000 a year*
Personal	• learn to *pilot a twin-engine prop plane before I'm 30* • lose *twenty pounds* by my birthday *(August 7th)* • complete a *ten-kilometer race* on *November 15th* • become more assertive *at work during weekly meetings*
Recreational	• own a *4-wheel-drive truck within two years* • take a vacation to *Hawaii next summer*
Financial	• save *$1,000* by *Thanksgiving*
Spiritual	• become more involved at *my house of worship* • take more time *every week* to reflect on my life

While the above example is a good one, it is only the first of three parts in setting and achieving goals. For the second part, you must break down each goal into separate steps that are even more specific and that also include time frames.

For example, under *Financial* (save $1,000 by Thanksgiving), this goal could be divided into several steps: put *$100 a month* into savings account; *work overtime on Mondays.* Again, notice that these "subgoals" are also specific.

The third and final step is to write these goals down and place them where you can see them often. A notebook or datebook is a good way to begin.

A Put an X by the sentence in each pair that states a specific, measurable goal.

_____   **1.** Take a trip to Paris with my friend Molly.

_____   Go to Paris with Molly by the end of next year.

_____   **2.** Lose ten pounds by the holidays.

_____   Go on a diet and begin exercising.

_____   **3.** Learn to work a computer and printer.

_____   Take computer lessons at the community center next month.

_____   **4.** Visit or call my family more often.

_____   Go to see one family member at least once a week.

_____   **5.** Paint my bedroom by the end of May.

_____   Redecorate my room using my favorite colors.

B Rewrite each goal so that it is specific and measurable and includes a time frame.

1. Practice the piano more.

_____

_____

_____

2. Read more often.

_____

_____

_____

C Using the chart on page 88, create subgoals—or steps—for each main
goal below.

Career　　　　accountant for a large corporation, earning $25,000 a year

Steps:　　_____

　　　　　　_____

　　　　　　_____

　　　　　　_____

Personal　　　complete a ten-kilometer race on November 15

Steps:　　_____

　　　　　　_____

　　　　　　_____

　　　　　　_____

Recreational　own a four-wheel-drive truck within two years

Steps:　　_____

　　　　　　_____

　　　　　　_____

　　　　　　_____

Financial　　save $1,000 by Thanksgiving

Steps:　　_____

　　　　　　_____

　　　　　　_____

　　　　　　_____

Spiritual　　become more involved at my house of worship

Steps:　　_____

　　　　　　_____

　　　　　　_____

　　　　　　_____

D Refer to the two goals you wrote on page 87. Write them under the categories where they would best fit. Then think about and write goals you might like to achieve in other categories.

Remember: **1.** Be specific.
2. Include a time frame.
3. Set goals that are measurable.

Career

_____

_____

_____

Personal

_____

_____

_____

Recreational

_____

_____

_____

Financial

_____

_____

_____

Spiritual

_____

_____

_____

E Choose five of the goals you wrote on the previous page. List each goal and then create specific steps for achieving it.

Career   Goal: _____

Steps: _____

                  _____

                  _____

                  _____

Personal   Goal: _____

Steps: _____

                  _____

                  _____

                  _____

Recreational Goal: _____

Steps: _____

                  _____

                  _____

                  _____

Financial   Goal: _____

Steps: _____

                  _____

                  _____

                  _____

Spiritual   Goal: _____

Steps: _____

                  _____

                  _____

                  _____

Test Units 5–8

Signs

A Write what each sign means.

1. _____

2. _____

3. _____

4. _____

5. _____

6. _____

Planning a Trip

B List five expenses you would need to include when planning a trip.

1. _____

2. _____

3. _____

4. _____

5. _____

Leasing an Apartment

C Number the steps 1 through 5 to show the order you would most logically follow when renting an apartment.

_____ 1. Determine what you can afford.

_____ 2. Look at several apartments.

_____ 3. Decide what kind of apartment you need or want.

_____ 4. Check ads for apartments.

_____ 5. Sign a lease.

Definitions

D Write a brief definition of each word.

1. utilities _____

2. budget _____

3. jury _____

4. refund _____

Social Services

E Read each question. Write the letter of the agency that answers the question.

a. Housing Authority   d. Welfare Assistance
b. Small Business Administration   e. Selective Service
c. Social Security   f. Internal Revenue

_____ 1. If you need some help buying food, where might you go?

_____ 2. Where could you go to get information about starting up a hot-dog stand?

_____ 3. Whom does an eighteen-year-old male contact?

_____ 4. Where would you go for help if you need a place to live?

_____ 5. When you turn sixty-five and want to know what benefits you can receive, whom would you contact?

End-of-Book Test

Employment Application

A Study the application. Then tell what mistakes the person made in each line.

EMPLOYMENT APPLICATION

1.   Date _June 22_

2.   Name _Rebecca_   _Ann_   _Powell_
                Last   First   Middle Initial

3.   Address _170 River Street_   _Chicago_
                   Number   Street

4.   _Illinois_
                   City   State   ZIP Code

5.   Phone _(312) 611-1212_ Social Security No. _____

6.   Years With Present Employer _$18,000_   Current Salary _2_

1. _____
2. _____
3. _____
4. _____
5. _____
6. _____

Paycheck Deductions

B Put an X in front of each word or phrase that is an example of a deduction that might be taken out of a paycheck.

_____ 1. health insurance   _____ 6. service charge

_____ 2. gross pay   _____ 7. state tax

_____ 3. FICA (Social Security)   _____ 8. overtime

_____ 4. take-home pay   _____ 9. net pay

_____ 5. withholding tax   _____ 10. city tax

Catalog Order

C Use the information that follows to complete the catalog order form.

You want to order a size large yellow T-shirt found on page 46 of the catalog. The item is number 22AF139. The shirt costs $18.99 plus $2.50 in shipping charges and $1.33 in taxes.

Name _____
         Last   First   Middle Initial

Address _____
         Number   Street

         City   State   ZIP Code

Page	Item No.	Item	Color	Size	Price

Subtotal	
Shipping	
Tax	
TOTAL	

Signs

D Write what each sign means.

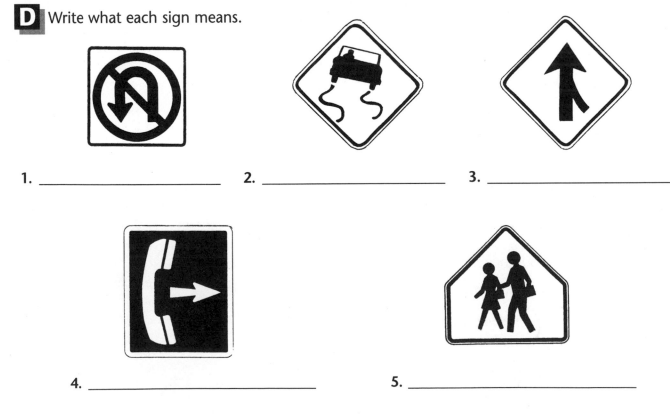

1. _____ 2. _____ 3. _____

4. _____   5. _____